LAND AND SEA TALES
FOR SCOUTS AND GUIDES

LAND AND SEA TALES

FOR SCOUTS AND GUIDES

BY

RUDYARD KIPLING

COMMISSIONER, BOY SCOUTS

MACMILLAN AND CO., LIMITED
ST. MARTIN'S STREET, LONDON
1923

PRINTED IN GREAT BRITAIN

PREFACE

To all to whom this little book may come—
    Health for yourselves and those you hold most
      dear!
Content abroad, and happiness at home,
    And—one grand secret in your private ear:—
    Nations have passed away and left no traces,
And History gives the naked cause of it—
    One single, simple reason in all cases;
They fell because their peoples were not fit.

Now, though your Body be mis-shapen, blind,
    Lame, feverish, lacking substance, power or
      skill,
Certain it is that men can school the Mind
    To school the sickliest Body to her will—
    As many have done, whose glory blazes still
Like mighty flames in meanest lanterns lit:
    Wherefore, we pray the crippled, weak and ill—
Be fit—be fit!   In mind at first be fit!

And, though your Spirit seem uncouth or small,
    Stubborn as clay or shifting as the sand,
Strengthen the Body, and the Body shall
    Strengthen the Spirit till she take command;

As a bold rider brings his horse in hand
At the tall fence, with voice and heel and bit,
   And leaps while all the field are at a stand.
Be fit—be fit!   In body next be fit!

     Nothing on earth—no Arts, no Gifts, nor
       Graces—
       No Fame, no Wealth—outweighs the want
        of it.
     This is the Law which every law embraces—
       Be fit—be fit!   In mind and body be fit!

The even heart that seldom slurs its beat—
   The cool head weighing what that heart de-
     sires—
The measuring eye that guides the hands and
     feet—
   The Soul unbroken when the Body tires—
   These are the things our weary world requires
Far more than superfluities of wit;
   Wherefore we pray you, sons of generous
     sires,
Be fit—be fit!   For Honour's sake be fit.

     There is one lesson at all Times and Places—
       One changeless Truth on all things changing
        writ,
     For boys and girls, men, women, nations,
       races—
       Be fit—be fit!   And once again, be fit!

CONTENTS

vii

WINNING THE VICTORIA CROSS

WINNING THE VICTORIA CROSS

THE history of the Victoria Cross has been told so often that it is only necessary to say that the Order was created by Queen Victoria on January 29th, 1856, in the year of the peace with Russia, when the new racing Cunard paddle-steamer *Persia* of three thousand tons was making thirteen knots between England and America, and all the world wondered at the advance of civilization and progress.

Any rank of the English Army, Navy, Reserve or Volunteer forces, from a duke to a negro, can wear on his left breast the little ugly bronze Maltese cross with the crowned lion atop and the inscription " For Valour " below, if he has only " performed some signal act of valour " or devotion to his country " in the presence of the enemy." Nothing else makes any difference; for it is explicitly laid down in the warrant that " neither rank, nor long service, nor wounds, nor any other circumstance whatsoever, save the merit of conspicuous bravery, shall be held to establish a sufficient claim to this Order."

3

There are many kinds of bravery, and if one looks through the records of the four hundred and eleven men, living and dead, that have held the Victoria Cross before the Great War, one finds instances of every imaginable variety of heroism.

There is bravery in the early morning, when it takes great courage even to leave warm blankets, let alone walk into dirt, cold and death; on foot and on horse; empty or fed; sick or well; coolness of brain that thinks out a plan at dawn and holds to it all through the long, murderous day; bravery of the mind that makes the jerking nerves hold still and do nothing except show a good example ; sheer reckless strength that hacks through a crowd of amazed men and comes out grinning on the other side; enduring spirit that wears through a long siege, never losing heart or manners or temper; quick, flashing bravery that heaves a lighted shell overboard or rushes the stockade while others are gaping at it; and the calculated craftsmanship that camps alone before the angry rifle-pit or shell-hole, and cleanly and methodically wipes out every soul in it.

Before the Great War, England dealt with many different peoples, and, generally speaking, all of them, Zulu, Malay, Maori, Burman, Boer, the little hillsman of the North-east Indian Frontier, Afreedi, Pathan, Biluch, the Arab of

East Africa and the Sudanese of the North of Africa and the rest, played a thoroughly good game. For this we owe them many thanks; since they showed us every variety of climate and almost every variety of attack, from long-range fire to hand-to-hand scrimmage; except, of course, the ordered movements of Continental armies and the scientific ruin of towns. . . . That came later and on the largest scale.

It is rather the fashion to look down on these little wars and to call them " military promenades " and so forth, but in reality no enemy can do much more than poison your wells, rush your camp, ambuscade you, kill you with his climate, fight you body to body, make you build your own means of communication under his fire, and horribly cut up your wounded. He may do this on a large or small scale, but the value of the teaching is the same.

It is in these rough-and-tumble affairs that many of the first Crosses were won; and some of the records for the far-away Crimea and the Indian Mutiny are well worth remembering, if only to show that valour never varies.

The Crimea was clean fighting as far as the enemy were concerned,—for the very old men say that no one could wish for better troops than the Russians of Inkerman and Alma,—but our own War Office then, as two generations later, helped the enemy with ignorant mismanagement and neglect. In the Mutiny of 1857 all India, Bengal and the North-West Provinces, seemed to be crumbling like sand-bag walls in flood, and wherever there were three or four Englishmen left, they had to kill or be killed till help came. Hundreds of Crosses must have been won then, had anybody had time to notice; for the average of work allowing for the improvements in man-killing machinery was as high as in the Great War.

For instance—this is a rather extensive and varied record—one man shut up in the Residency at Lucknow stole out three times at the risk of his life to get cattle for the besieged to eat. Later, he extinguished a fire near a powder-magazine and a month afterwards put out another fire. Then he led twelve men to capture two guns which were wrecking the Residency at close range. Next day he captured an outlying position full of mutineers; three days later he captured another gun, and finished up by capturing a fourth. So he got his Cross.

Another young man was a lieutenant in the Southern Mahratta Horse, and a full regiment of mutineers broke into his part of the world, upsetting the minds of the people. He collected some loyal troopers, chased the regiment eighty miles, stormed the fort they had taken refuge in, and killed, captured or wounded every soul there.

Then there was a lance-corporal who afterwards rose to be Lieutenant-Colonel. He was the enduring type of man, for he won his Cross merely for taking a hand in every fight that came along through nearly seventy consecutive days.

There were also two brothers who earned the Cross about six times between them for leading forlorn hopes and such-like. Likewise there was a private of " persuasive powers and cheerful disposition," so the record says, who was cut off with nine companions in a burning house while the mutineers were firing in at the windows. He, however, cheerfully persuaded the enemy to retire, and in the end all his party were saved through his practical " cheerfulness." He must have been a man worth knowing.

And there was a little man in the Sutherland Highlanders—a private who eventually became a Major-General. In one attack near Lucknow he killed eleven men with his claymore, which is a heating sort of weapon to handle.

Even he was not more thorough than two troopers who rode to the rescue of their Colonel, cut off and knocked down by mutineers. They helped him to rise, and they must have been annoyed, for the three of them killed all the mutineers—about fifty.

Then there was a negro captain of the foretop, William Hall, R.N., who with two other negroes,

Samuel Hodge and W. J. Gordon of the 4th
and 1st West Indian Infantry, came up the river
with the Naval Brigade from Calcutta to work
big guns. They worked them so thoroughly
that each got a Cross. They must have done a
good deal, for no one is quite so crazy reckless
as a West Indian negro when he is really excited.

There was a man in the Mounted Police who
with sixty horsemen charged one thousand
mutineers and broke them up. And so the tale
runs on.

Three Bengal Civilian Government officers
were, I believe, the only strict non-combatants
who ever received the Cross. As a matter of
fact they had to fight with the rest, but the story
of " Lucknow " Kavanagh's adventures in dis-
guise, of Ross Mangle's heroism after the first
attempt to relieve the Little House at Arrah had
failed (Arrah was a place where ten white men and
fifty-six loyal natives barricaded themselves in a
billiard-room in a garden and stood the siege of
three regiments of mutineers for three weeks),
and of McDonnel's cool-headedness in the retreat
down the river, are things that ought to be told
by themselves. Almost any one can fight well
on the winning side, but those men who can patch
up a thoroughly bad business and pull it off in
some sort of shape, are most to be respected.

Army chaplains and doctors are officially

supposed to be non-combatants—they are not really so—but about twenty years after the Mutiny a chaplain was decorated under circumstances that made it impossible to overlook his bravery. Still, I do not think he quite cared for the publicity. He was a regimental chaplain—in action a chaplain is generally supposed to stay with or near the doctor—and he seems to have drifted up close to a cavalry charge, for he helped a wounded officer of the Ninth Lancers into an ambulance. He was then going about his business when he found two troopers who had tumbled into a water-course all mixed with their horses, and a knot of Afghans were hurrying to attend to them. The record says that he rescued both men, but the tale, as I heard it unofficially, declares that he found a revolver somewhere with which he did excellent work while the troopers were struggling out of the ditch. This seems very possible, for the Afghans do not leave disabled men without the strongest hint, and I know that in nine cases out of ten if you want a coherent account of what happened in an action you had better ask the chaplain or the Roman Catholic priest of a battalion.

But it is difficult to get details. I have met perhaps a dozen or so of V.C.'s, and in every case they explained that they did the first thing that came to their hand without worrying about alternatives. One man headed a charge into a mass of Afghans, who are very good fighters so long as they stay interested in their work, and cut down five of them. All he said was: " Well, they were there, and they couldn't go away. What was a man to do? Write 'em a note and ask 'em to shift?"

Another man I questioned was a doctor. Army doctors, by the way, have special opportunities for getting Crosses. Their duty compels them to stay somewhere within touch of the firing-line, and most of them run right up and lie down, keeping an eye on the wounded.

It is a heart-breaking thing for a doctor who has pulled a likely young private of twenty-three through typhoid fever and set him on his feet and watched him develop, to see the youngster wasted with a casual bullet. It must have been this feeling that made my friend do the old, splendid thing that never grows stale—rescue a wounded man under fire. He won this Cross, but all he said was: " *I* didn't want any unauthorized consultations—or amputations—while I was Medical Officer in charge. 'Tisn't etiquette."

His own head was very nearly blown off as he was tying up an artery—for it was blind, bad bush-fighting, with puffs of smoke popping in and out among the high grass and never a man visible—but he only grunted when his helmet was cracked across by a bullet, and went on tightening the tourniquet.

As I have hinted, in most of our little affairs before the war, the enemy knew nothing about the Geneva Convention or the treatment of wounded, but fired at a doctor on his face value as a white man. One cannot blame them—it was their custom, but it was exceedingly awkward when our doctors took care of their wounded who did not understand these things and tried to go on fighting in hospital.

There is an interesting tale of a wounded Sudanese — what our soldiers used to call a " fuzzy " — who was carefully attended to in a hospital after a fight. As soon as he had any strength again, he proposed to a native orderly that they two should massacre all the infidel wounded in the other beds. The orderly did not see it; so, when the doctor came in he found the " Fuzzy " was trying to work out his plan single-handed. The doctor had a very unpleasant scuffle with that simple-minded man, but, at last, he slipped the chloroform-bag over his nose. The man understood bullets and was not afraid of them; but this magic smelly stuff that sent him to sleep, cowed him altogether, and he gave no more trouble in the ward.

So a doctor's life is always a little hazardous and, besides his professional duties, he may find

himself senior officer in charge of what is left of
the command, if the others have been shot down.
As doctors are always full of theories, I believe
they rather like this chance of testing them.
Sometimes doctors have run out to help a mortally
wounded man of their battalion, because they
know that he may have last messages to give, and
it eases him to die with some human being holding his hand. This is a most noble thing to do
under fire, because it means sitting still among
bullets. Chaplains have done it also, but it is
part of what they reckon as their regular duty.

Another V.C. of my acquaintance — he was
anything but a doctor or a chaplain—once saved
a trooper whose horse had been killed. His
method was rather original. The man was on
foot and the enemy—Zulus this time—was coming
down at a run, and the trooper said, very decently,
that he did not see his way to perilling his officer's
life by double-weighting the only available horse.

To this his officer replied: " If you don't get
up behind me, I'll get off and give you such a
licking as you've never had in your life." The
man was more afraid of fists than of assagais, and
the good horse pulled them both out of the scrape.
Now by our Regulations an officer who insults or
" threatens with violence " a subordinate in the
Service is liable to lose his commission and to be
declared " incapable of serving the King in any

capacity"; but for some reason or other the trooper never reported his superior.

The humour and the honour of fighting are by no means all on one side. A good many years ago there was a war in New Zealand against the Maoris, who, though they tortured prisoners and occasionally ate a man, liked fighting for its own sake. One of their chiefs cut off a detachment of our men in a stockade where he might have starved them out, and eaten them at leisure later. But word reached him that they were short of provisions, and so he sent in a canoeful of pig and potatoes with the message that it was no fun to play that game with weak men, and he would be happy to meet them after rest and a full meal. There are many cases in which men, very young as a rule, have forced their way through a stockade of thorns that hook or bamboos that cut and held on in the face of heavy fire or just so long as served to bring up their comrades. Those who have done this say that getting in is exciting enough, but the bad time, when the minutes drag like hours, lies between the first scuffle with the angry faces in the smoke, and the " Hi, get out o' this!" that shows that the others of our side are tumbling up behind. They say it is as bad as football when you get off the ball just as slowly as you dare, so that your own side may have time to come up.

Most men, after they have been shot over a little, only want a lead to do good work; so the result of a young man's daring is often out of all proportion to his actual performances.

Here is a case which never won notice because very few people talked about it—a case of the courage of Ulysses, one might say.

A column of troops, heavily weighted with sick and wounded, had drifted into a bad place— a pass where an enemy, hidden behind rocks, were picking them off at known ranges, as they retreated. Half a battalion was acting as rear-guard—company after company facing about on the narrow road and trying to keep down the wicked, flickering fire from the hill-sides. And it was twilight; and it was cold and raining; and it was altogether horrible for every one.

Presently, the rear-guard began to fire a little too quickly and to hurry back to the main body a little too soon, and the bearers put down the ambulances a little too often, and looked on each side of the road for possible cover. Altogether, there were the makings of a nasty little breakdown —and after that would come primitive slaughter.

A boy whom I knew was acting command of one company that was specially bored and sulky, and there were shouts from the column of " Hurry up! Hurry there!" neither necessary nor soothing. He kept his men in hand as well as he could, hitting down rifles when they fired wild, till some one along the line shouted: " What on earth are you fellows waiting so long for?"

Then my friend—I am rather proud that he was my friend—hunted for his pipe and tobacco, filled the bowl *in* his pocket because, he said afterwards, he didn't want any one to see how his hand shook, lit a fuzee, and shouted back between very short puffs: " Hold on a minute. I'm lighting my pipe."

There was a roar of rather crackly laughter and the company joker said: " Since you *are* so pressin', I think I'll 'ave a draw meself."

I don't believe either pipe was smoked out, but—and this is a very big but—the little bit of acting steadied the company, and the news of it ran down the line, and even the wounded in the doolies laughed, and every one felt better. Whether the enemy heard the laughing, or was impressed by the even " one-two-three-four " firing that followed it, will never be known, but the column came to camp at the regulation step and not at a run, with very few casualties. That is what one may call the courage of the much-enduring Ulysses, but the only comment that I ever heard on the affair was the boy's own, and all *he* said was: " It was transpontine (which means theatrical), but necessary."

Of course he must have been a good boy from

the beginning, for little bits of pure inspiration seldom come to or are acted upon by slovens, self-indulgent or undisciplined people. I have not yet met one V.C. who had not strict notions about washing and shaving and keeping himself decent on his way through the civilized world, whatever he may have done outside it.

Indeed, it is very curious, after one has known hundreds of young men and young officers, to sit still at a distance and watch them come forward to success in their profession. Somehow, the clean and considerate man mostly seems to take hold of circumstances at the right end.

One of the youngest of the V.C.'s of his time I used to know distantly as a beautiful being whom they called Aide - de - Camp to a big official in India. So far as strangers could judge, his duties consisted in wearing a uniform faced with blue satin, and in seeing that every one was looked after at the dances and dinners. He would wander about smiling, with eyes at the back of his head, introducing men who were strangers and a little uncomfortable, to girls whose dance-cards were rather empty ; taking old and un-interesting women into supper, and tucking them into their carriages afterwards; or pleasantly steer-ing white-whiskered native officers all covered with medals and half-blind with confusion through the maze of a big levee into the presence of the

Viceroy or Commander-in-Chief, or whoever it was they were being presented to.

After a few years of this work, his chance came, and he made the most of it. We were then smoking out a nest of caravan-raiders, slave-dealers, and general thieves who lived somewhere under the Karakoram Mountains among glaciers about sixteen thousand feet above sea-level. The mere road to the place was too much for many mules, for it ran by precipices and round rock-curves and over roaring, snow-fed rivers.

The enemy—they were called Kanjuts—had fortified themselves in a place nearly as impregnable as nature and man could make it. One position was on the top of a cliff about twelve hundred feet high, whence they could roll stones directly on the head of any attacking force. Our men objected to the stones much more than to the rifle-fire. They were camped in a river-bed at the bottom of an icy pass with some three tiers of these cliff-like defences above them, and the Kanjuts on each tier were very well armed. To make all specially pleasant, it was December.

This ex-aide-de-camp happened to be a good mountaineer, and he was told off with a hundred native troops, Goorkhas and Dogra Sikhs, to climb up into the top tier of the fortifications. The only way of arriving was to follow a sort of shoot in the cliff-face which the enemy had worn smooth by throwing rocks down. Even in daylight, in peace, and with good guides, it would have been fair mountaineering.

He went up in the dark, by eye and guess, against some two thousand Kanjuts very much at war with him. When he had climbed eight hundred feet almost perpendicular he found he had to come back, because even he and his Goorkha cragsmen could find no way.

He returned to the river-bed and tried again in a new place, working his men up between avalanches of stones that slid along and knocked people over. When he struggled to the top he had to take his men into the forts with the bayonet and the *kukri*, the little Goorkha knife. The attack was so utterly bold and unexpected that it broke the hearts of the enemy and practically ended the campaign ; and if you could see the photograph of the place you would understand why.

It was hard toe-nail and finger-nail crag-climbing under fire, and the men behind him were not regulars, but what are called Imperial Service troops — men raised by the semi-independent kings and used to defend the frontier. They enjoyed themselves immensely, and the little aide-de-camp got a deserved Victoria Cross. The courage of Ulysses again ; for he had to think as he climbed, and until he was directly underneath the fortifications, one chance-hopping boulder might just have planed his men off all along the line.

But there is a heroism beyond all, for which no Victoria Cross is ever given, because there is no official enemy nor any sort of firing, except one volley in the early morning at some spot where the noise does not echo into the newspapers.

It is necessary from time to time to send unarmed men into No Man's Land and the Back of Beyond across the Khudajanta Khan (The Lord-knows-where) Mountains, just to find out what is going on there among people who some day or other may become dangerous enemies.

The understanding is that if the men return with their reports so much the better for them. They may then receive some sort of decoration, given, so far as the public can make out, for no real reason. If they do not come back—and people disappear very mysteriously at the Back of Beyond—that is their own concern, and no questions will be asked, and no enquiries made.

They tell a tale of one man who, some years ago, strayed into No Man's Land to see how things were, and met a very amiable set of people, who asked him to a round of dinners and lunches and dances. And all that time he knew, and they knew that he knew, that his hosts were debating between themselves whether they should suffer him to live till next morning, and if they decided not to let him live, in what way they should wipe him out most quietly.

The only consideration that made them hesitate was that they could not tell from his manner whether there were five hundred Englishmen within a few miles of him or no Englishmen at all within five hundred miles of him ; and, as matters stood at that moment, they could not very well go out to look and make sure.

So he danced and dined with those pleasant, merry folk,—all good friends,—and talked about hunting and shooting and so forth, never knowing when the polite servants behind his chair would turn into the firing-party. At last his hosts decided, without rude words said, to let him go ; and when they made up their minds they did it very handsomely ; for, you must remember, there is no malice borne on either side in that game.

They gave him a farewell banquet and drank his health, and he thanked them for his delightful visit, and they said: " *So* glad you're glad. *Au revoir*," and he came away looking a little bored.

Later on, so the tale runs, his hosts discovered that their guest had been given up for lost by his friends in England, where no one ever expected to see him again. Then they were sorry that they had not put him against a wall and shot him.

That is a case of the cold-blooded courage

worked up to after years of training—courage of mind forcing the body through an unpleasant situation for the sake of the game.

When all is said and done, courage of mind is the finest thing any one can hope to attain to. A weak or undisciplined soul is apt to become reckless under strain (which is only being afraid the wrong way about), or to act for its own immediate advantage. For this reason the Victoria Cross is jealously guarded, and if there be suspicion that the man is playing to the gallery or out pot-hunting for medals, as they call it, he is often left to head his charges and rescue his wounded all over again as a guarantee of good faith.

In the Great War there was very little suspicion, or chance, of gallery-play for the V.C., because there was ample opportunity and, very often, strong necessity, for a man to repeat his performances several times over. Moreover, he was generally facing much deadlier weapons than mere single rifles or edged tools, and the rescue of wounded under fire was, by so much, a more serious business. But one or two War V.C.'s of my acquaintance have told me that if you can manage the little matter of keeping your head, it is not as difficult as it sounds to get on the blind side of a machine-gun, or to lie out under its lowest line of fire, where, they say, you are " quite comfortable if you don't fuss." Also, every V.C. of the Great War I have spoken to has been rather careful to explain that he won his Cross because what he did happened to be done when and where some one could notice it. Thousands of men they said did just the same, but in places where there were no observers. And that is true; for the real spirit of the Army changes very little through the years.

Men are taught to volunteer for anything and everything; going out quietly after, not before, the authorities have filled their place. They are also instructed that it is cowardly, it is childish, and it is cheating to neglect or scamp the plain work immediately in front of them, the duties they are trusted to do, for the sake of stepping aside to snatch at what to an outsider may resemble fame or distinction. Above all, their own hard equals, whose opinion is the sole opinion worth having, are always sitting unofficially in judgment on them.

The Order itself is a personal decoration, and the honour and glory of it belongs to the wearer; but he can only win it by forgetting himself, his own honour and glory, and by working for something beyond and outside and apart from his own self. And there seems to be no other way in which you get anything in this world worth the keeping.

THE WAY THAT HE TOOK

THE WAY THAT HE TOOK

Almost every word of this story is based on fact. The Boer War of 1899–1902 was a very small one as wars were reckoned, and was fought without any particular malice, but it taught our men the practical value of scouting in the field. They were slow to learn at the outset, and it cost them many unnecessary losses, as is always the case when men think they can do their work without taking trouble beforehand.

THE guns of the Field-Battery were ambushed behind white-thorned mimosas, scarcely taller than their wheels, that marked the line of a dry nullah; and the camp pretended to find shade under a clump of gums planted as an experiment by some Minister of Agriculture. One small hut, reddish stone with a tin roof, stood where the single track of the railway split into a siding. A rolling plain of red earth, speckled with loose stones and sugar-bush, ran northward to the scarps and spurs of a range of little hills—all barren and exaggerated in the heat-haze. Southward, the level lost itself in a tangle of scrub-furred hillocks, upheaved without purpose or order, seared and blackened by the strokes of

25

the careless lightning, seamed down their sides
with spent watercourses, and peppered from base
to summit with stones—riven, piled, scattered
stones.   Far away, to the eastward, a line of
blue-grey mountains, peaked and horned, lifted
itself over the huddle of the tortured earth.   It
was the only thing that held steady through the
liquid mirage.   The nearer hills detached themselves from the plain, and swam forward like
islands in a milky ocean.   While the Major
stared through puckered eyelids, Leviathan himself waded through the far shallows of it—a
black and formless beast.

   " That," said the Major, " must be the guns
coming back."   He had sent out two guns,
nominally for exercise—actually to show the
loyal Dutch that there was artillery near the
railway if any patriot thought fit to tamper with
it.   Chocolate smears, looking as though they
had been swept with a besom through the raffle
of stones, wandered across the earth—unbridged,
ungraded, unmetalled.   They were the roads
to the brown mud huts, one in each valley, that
were officially styled farm-houses.   At very long
intervals a dusty Cape-cart or a tilted wagon
would move along them, and men, dirtier than
the dirt, would come to sell fruit or scraggy
sheep.   At night the farm-houses were lighted
up in a style out of all keeping with Dutch

economy; the scrub would light itself on some
far headland, and the house-lights twinkled in
reply. Three or four days later the Major
would read bad news in the Capetown papers
thrown to him from the passing troop trains.

The guns and their escort changed from
Leviathan to the likeness of wrecked boats,
their crews struggling beside them. Presently
they took on their true shape, and lurched into
camp amid clouds of dust.

The Mounted Infantry escort set about its
evening meal; the hot air filled with the scent
of burning wood; sweating men rough-dried
sweating horses with wisps of precious forage;
the sun dipped behind the hills, and they heard
the whistle of a train from the south.

" What's that?" said the Major, slipping
into his coat. The decencies had not yet left
him.

" Ambulance train," said the Captain of
Mounted Infantry, raising his glasses. " I'd
like to talk to a woman again, but it won't stop
here. . . . It *is* stopping, though, and making
a beastly noise. Let's look."

The engine had sprung a leaky tube, and
ran lamely into the siding. It would be two
or three hours at least before she could be
patched up.

Two doctors and a couple of Nursing Sisters

stood on the rear platform of a carriage. The Major explained the situation, and invited them to tea.

"We were just going to ask *you*," said the medical Major of the ambulance train.

"No, come to our camp. Let the men see a woman again!" he pleaded.

Sister Dorothy, old in the needs of war, for all her twenty-four years, gathered up a tin of biscuits and some bread and butter new cut by the orderlies. Sister Margaret picked up the teapot, the spirit-lamp, and a water-bottle.

"Capetown water," she said with a nod. "Filtered too. *I* know Karroo water." She jumped down lightly on to the ballast.

"What do you know about the Karroo, Sister?" said the Captain of Mounted Infantry, indulgently, as a veteran of a month's standing. He understood that all that desert as it seemed to him was called by that name.

She laughed. "This is my home. I was born out they-ah—just behind that big range of hills—out Oudtshorn way. It's only sixty miles from here. Oh, how good it is!"

She slipped the Nurses' cap from her head, tossed it through the open car-window, and drew a breath of deep content. With the sinking of the sun the dry hills had taken life and glowed against the green of the horizon.

They rose up like jewels in the utterly clear air, while the valleys between flooded with purple shadow. A mile away, stark-clear, withered rocks showed as though one could touch them with the hand, and the voice of a native herd-boy in charge of a flock of sheep came in clear and sharp over twice that distance. Sister Margaret devoured the huge spaces with eyes unused to shorter ranges, snuffed again the air that has no equal under God's skies, and, turning to her companion, said: " What do *you* think of it? "

" I am afraid I'm rather singular," he replied. " Most of us hate the Karroo. I used to, but it grows on one somehow. I suppose it's the lack of fences and roads that's so fascinating. And when one gets back from the railway—— "

" You're quite right," she said, with an emphatic stamp of her foot. " People come to Matjesfontein—ugh!—with their lungs, and they live opposite the railway station and that new hotel, and they think *that's* the Karroo. They say there isn't anything in it. It's *full* of life when you really get into it. You see that? I'm *so* glad. D'you know, you're the first English officer I've heard who has spoken a good word for my country? "

" I'm glad I pleased you," said the Captain, looking into Sister Margaret's black-lashed grey eyes under the heavy brown hair shot with grey where it rolled back from the tanned forehead. This kind of nurse was new in his experience. The average Sister did not lightly stride over rolling stones, and—was it possible that her easy pace up-hill was beginning to pump him? As she walked, she hummed joyously to herself, a queer catchy tune of one line several times repeated:

> Vat jou goet en trek, Ferriera,
> Vat jou goet en trek.

It ran off with a little trill that sounded like:

> Zwaar draa, alle en de ein kant;
> Jannie met de hoepel bein![1]

" Listen!" she said, suddenly. " What was that?"

" It must be a wagon on the road.   I heard the whip, I think."

" Yes, but you didn't hear the wheels, did you?   It's a little bird that makes just that noise, ' Whe-ew '!" she duplicated it perfectly. " We call it "—she gave the Dutch name, which did not, of course, abide with the Captain. " We must have given him a scare!   You hear him in the early mornings when you are sleeping

---

[1] Pack your kit and trek, Ferriera,
Pack your kit and trek.
A long pull, all on one side,
Johnnie with the lame leg.

in the wagons.   It's just like the noise of a whip--
lash, isn't it?"

They entered the Major's tent a little behind
the others, who were discussing the scanty news
of the Campaign.

" Oh, no," said Sister Margaret coolly, bending over the spirit-lamp, " the Transvaalers will
stay round Kimberley and try to put Rhodes in
a cage.   But, of course, if a commando gets
through to De Aar they will all rise———— "

" You think so, Sister?" said the medical
Major, deferentially.

" I know so.   They will rise anywhere in the
Colony if a commando comes actually to them.
Presently they will rise in Prieska—if it is only
to steal the forage at Van Wyk's Vlei.   Why
not?"

" We get most of our opinions of the war from
Sister Margaret," said the civilian doctor of the
train.   " It's all new to me, but, so far, all her
prophecies have come true."

A few months ago that doctor had retired
from practice to a country house in rainy England,
his fortune made and, as he tried to believe, his
life-work done.   Then the bugles blew, and,
rejoicing at the change, he found himself, his
experience, and his fine bedside manner, buttoned
up in a black-tabbed khaki coat, on a hospital
train that covered eleven hundred miles a week,

carried a hundred wounded each trip and dealt him more experience in a month than he had ever gained in a year of home practice.

Sister Margaret and the Captain of Mounted Infantry took their cups outside the tent. The Captain wished to know something more about her. Till that day he had believed South Africa to be populated by sullen Dutchmen and slack-waisted women; and in some clumsy fashion betrayed the belief.

"Of course, you don't see any others where you are," said Sister Margaret, leniently, from her camp-chair. "They are all at the war. I have two brothers, and a nephew, my sister's son, and—oh, I can't count my cousins." She flung her hands outward with a curiously un-English gesture. "And then, too, you have never been off the railway. You have only seen Capetown? All the schel—all the useless people are there. You should see *our* country beyond the ranges— out Oudtshorn way. We grow fruit and vines. It is much prettier, *I* think, than Paarl."

"I'd like to very much. I may be stationed in Africa after the war is over."

"Ah, but we know the English officers. They say that this is a ' beastly country,' and they do not know how to—to be nice to people. Shall I tell you? There was an aide-de-camp at Government House three years ago. He sent out invitations to dinner to Piet—to Mr. Van der Hooven's wife.   And she had been dead eight years, and Van der Hooven—he has the big farms round Craddock—just then was thinking of changing his politics, you see—he was against the Government,—and taking a house in Cape-town, because of the Army meat contracts.   That was why, you see?"

"I see," said the Captain, to whom this was all Greek.

"Piet was a little angry—not much—but he went to Capetown, and that aide-de-camp had made a joke about it—about inviting the dead woman—in the Civil Service Club.   You see? So of *course* the opposition there told Van der Hooven that the aide-de-camp had said he could not remember all the old Dutch vrows that had died, and so Piet Van der Hooven went away angry, and now he is more hot than ever against the Government.   If you stay with us you must not be like *that*.   You see?"

"I won't," said the Captain, seriously.   "What a night it is, Sister!"   He dwelt lovingly on the last word, as men did in South Africa.

The soft darkness had shut upon them unawares and the world had vanished.   There was not so much breeze as a slow motion of the whole dry air under the vault of the immeasurably deep heavens.   "Look up," said the Captain;

D

" doesn't it make you feel as if we were tumbling down into the stars—all upside down?"

" Yes," said Sister Margaret, tilting her head back. " It is always like that. I know. And those are *our* stars."

They burned with a great glory, large as the eyes of cattle by lamp-light; planet after planet of the mild Southern sky. As the Captain said, one seemed to be falling from out the hidden earth sheer through space, between them.

" Now, when I was little," Sister Margaret began very softly, " there was one day in the week at home that was all our own. We could get up as soon as we liked after midnight, and there was the basket in the kitchen—our food. We used to go out at three o'clock sometimes, my two brothers, my sisters, and the two little ones—out into the Karroo for all the day. All —the—long—day. First we built a fire, and then we made a kraal for the two little ones—a kraal of thorn bushes so that they should not be bitten by anything. You see? Often we made the kraal before morning—when those "—she jerked her firm chin at the stars—" were just going out. Then we old ones went hunting lizards—and snakes and birds and centipedes, and all that sort of nice thing. Our father collected them. He gave us half-a-crown for a spuugh-slange—a kind of snake. You see?"

"How old were you?" Snake-hunting did not strike the Captain as a safe amusement for the young.

"I was eleven then—or ten, perhaps, and the little ones were two and three. Why? Then we came back to eat, and we sat under a rock all afternoon. It was hot, you see, and we played —we played with the stones and the flowers. You should see our Karroo in spring! All flowers! All our flowers! Then we came home, carrying the little ones on our backs asleep— came home through the dark—just like this night. That was our own day! Oh, the good days! We used to watch the meer-cats playing, too, and the little buck. When I was at Guy's, learning to nurse, how home-sick that made me!"

"But what a splendid open-air life!" said the Captain.

"Where else *is* there to live except the open air?" said Sister Margaret, looking off into twenty thousand square miles of it with eyes that burned.

"You're quite right."

"I'm sorry to interrupt you two," said Sister Dorothy, who had been talking to the gunner Major; "but the guard says we shall be ready to go in a few minutes. Major Devine and Dr. Johnson have gone down already."

"Very good, Sister. We'll follow." The

Captain rose unwillingly and made for the worn path from the camp to the rail.

" Isn't there another way?" said Sister Margaret. Her grey nursing gown glimmered like some big moth's wing.

" No. I'll bring a lantern. It's quite safe."

" I did not think of *that*," she said with a laugh; " only *we* never come home by the way we left it when we live in the Karroo. If any one —suppose you had dismissed a Kaffir, or got him sjamboked,[1] and he saw you go out? He would wait for you to come back on a tired horse, and then. . . . You see? But, of course, in England where the road is all walled, it is different. How funny! Even when we were little we learned never to come home by the way we went out."

" Very good," said the Captain, obediently. It made the walk longer, and he approved of that.

" That's a curious sort of woman," said the Captain to the Major, as they smoked a lonely pipe together when the train had gone.

" *You* seemed to think so."

" Well—I couldn't monopolize Sister Dorothy in the presence of my senior officer. What was she like?"

" Oh, it came out that she knew a lot of my people in London. She's the daughter of a chap in the next county to us, too."

*   *   *   *   *

[1] Beaten.

The General's flag still flew before his unstruck tent to amuse Boer binoculars, and loyal lying correspondents still telegraphed accounts of his daily work. But the General himself had gone to join an army a hundred miles away; drawing off, from time to time, every squadron, gun and company that he dared. His last words to the few troops he left behind covered the entire situation.

" If you can bluff 'em till we get round 'em up north to tread on their tails, it's all right. If you can't, they'll probably eat you up. Hold 'em as long as you can."

So the skeleton remnant of the brigade lay close among the kopjes till the Boers, not seeing them in force on the sky-line, feared that they might have learned the rudiments of war. They rarely disclosed a gun, for the reason that they had so few; they scouted by fours and fives instead of clattering troops and chattering companies, and where they saw a too obvious way opened to attack they, lacking force to drive it home, looked elsewhere. Great was the anger in the Boer commando across the river—the anger and unease.

" The reason is they have so few men," the loyal farmers reported, all fresh from selling melons to the camp, and drinking Queen Victoria's health in good whisky. " They have no horses—only what they call Mounted Infantry.

They are afraid of us. They try to make us friends by giving us brandy. Come on and shoot them. Then you will see us rise and cut the line."

" Yes, we know how you rise, you Colonials," said the Boer commandant above his pipe. " We know what has come to all your promises from Beaufort West, and even from De Aar. *We* do the work—all the work,—and you kneel down with your parsons and pray for our success. What good is that? The President has told you a hundred times God is on our side. Why do you worry Him? We did not send you Mausers and ammunition for *that*."

" We kept our commando-horses ready for six months—and forage is very dear. We sent all our young men," said an honoured member of local society.

" A few here and a few servants there. What is that? You should have risen down to the sea all together."

" But you were so quick. Why did not you wait the year? We were not ready, Jan."

" That is a lie. All you Cape people lie. You want to save your cattle and your farms. Wait till *our* flag flies from here to Port Elizabeth and you shall see what you will save when the President learns how you have risen—you clever Cape people."

The saddle-coloured sons of the soil looked down their noses. " Yes—it is true. Some of our farms are close to the line. They say at Worcester and in the Paarl that many soldiers are always coming in from the sea. One must think of that—at least till they are shot. But we know there are very few in front of you here. Give them what you gave the fools at Stormberg, and you will see how we can shoot rooineks." [1]

" Yes. I know that cow. She is always going to calve. Get away. I am answerable to the President—not to the Cape."

But the information stayed in his mind, and, not being a student of military works, he made a plan to suit. The tall kopje on which the English had planted their helio-station commanded the more or less open plain to the northward, but did not command the five-mile belt of broken country between that and the outmost English pickets, some three miles from camp. The Boers had established themselves very comfortably among these rock-ridges and scrub-patches, and the " great war " drizzled down to long shots and longer stalking. The young bloods wanted rooineks to shoot, and said so.

" See here," quoth the experienced Jan van Staden that evening to as many of his commando as cared to listen. " You youngsters from the

[1] Red necks—English soldiers.

Colony talk a lot. Go and turn the rooineks out of their kopjes to-night. Eh? Go and take their bayonets from them and stick them into them. Eh? You don't go!" He laughed at the silence round the fire.

"Jan—Jan," said one young man appealingly, "don't make mock of us."

"I thought that was what you wanted so badly. No? Then listen to me. Behind us the grazing is bad. We have too many cattle here." (They had been stolen from farmers who had been heard to express fears of defeat.) "To-morrow, by the sky's look, it will blow a good wind. So, to-morrow early I shall send all our cattle north to the new grazing. That will make a great dust for the English to see from their helio yonder." He pointed to a winking night-lamp stabbing the darkness with orders to an out-lying picket. "With the cattle we will send all our women. Yes, all the women and the wagons we can spare, and the lame ponies and the broken carts we took from Andersen's farm. That will make a big dust—the dust of our retreat. Do you see?"

They saw and approved, and said so.

"Good. There are many men here who want to go home to their wives. I shall let thirty of them away for a week. Men who wish to do this will speak to me to-night." (This meant

that Jan needed money, and furlough would be
granted on strictly business lines.)   " These men
will look after the cattle and see that they make a
great dust for a long way.   They will run about
behind the cattle showing their guns, too.   So
that, if the wind blows well, will be our retreat.
The cattle will feed beyond Koopman's Kop."

" No good water there," growled a farmer
who knew that section.   " Better go on to
Zwartpan.   It is always sweet at Zwartpan."

The commando discussed the point for twenty
minutes.   It was much more serious than shooting rooineks.   Then Jan went on:

" When the rooineks see our retreat they may
all come into our kopjes together.   If so, good.
But it is tempting God to expect such a favour.
I think they will first send some men to scout."
He grinned broadly, twisting the English word.
" Almighty!   To scoot!   They have none of
that new sort of rooinek that they used at Sunny-
side."   (Jan meant an incomprehensible animal
from a place called Australia across the Southern
seas who played what they knew of the war-game
to kill.)   " They have only some Mounted Infantry,"—again he used the English words.
" They were once a Red-jacket regiment, so their
scoots will stand up bravely to be shot at."

" Good—good, we will shoot them," said a
youngster from Stellenbosch, who had come up

on free pass as a Capetown excursionist just before the war to a farm on the border, where his
aunt was taking care of his horse and rifle.

" But if you shoot their scoots I will sjambok
you myself," said Jan, amid roars of laughter.
" We must let them *all* come into the kopjes to
look for us; and I pray God will not allow any
of us to be tempted to shoot them.   They will
cross the ford in front of their camp.   They
will come along the road—so!"   He imitated
with ponderous arms the Army style of riding.
" They will trot up the road this way and that
way "—here he snaked his hard finger in the dust
—" between kopjes, till they come here, where
they can see the plain and all our cattle going
away.   Then they will *all* come in close together.
Perhaps they will even fix their bayonets.   *We*
shall be up here behind the rock—there and
there."   He pointed to two flat-topped kopjes,
one on either side of the road, some eight hundred
yards away.   " That is our place.   We will go
there before sunrise.   Remember we must be careful to let the very last of the rooineks pass before
we begin shooting.   They will come along a little
careful at first.   But we do not shoot.   Then they
will see our fires and the fresh horse-dung, so they
will know we have gone on.   They will run together
and talk and point and shout in this nice open place.
Then we begin shooting them from above."

"Yes, uncle, but if the scoots see nothing and there are no shots and we let them go back quite quiet, they will think it was a trick. Perhaps the main body may never come here at all. Even rooineks learn in time—and so we may lose even the scoots."

"I have thought of that too," said Jan, with slow contempt, as the Stellenbosch boy delivered his shot. "If you had been *my* son I should have sjamboked you more when you were a youngster. I shall put *you* and four or five more on the Nek [the pass], where the road comes from their camp into these kopjes. You go there before it is light. Let the scoots pass in or I will sjambok you myself. When the scoots come back after seeing nothing here, then you may shoot them, but not till they have passed the Nek and are on the straight road back to their camp again. Do you understand? Repeat what I have said, so that I shall know."

The youth obediently repeated his orders.

"Kill their officers if you can. If not, no great matter, because the scoots will run to camp with the news that our kopjes are empty. Their helio-station will see your party trying to hold the Nek so hard—and all that time they will see our dust out yonder, and they will think you are the rear-guard, and they will think *we* are escaping. They will be angry."

" Yes—yes, uncle, we see," from a dozen
elderly voices.

" But this calf does not. Be silent! They
will shoot at you, Niclaus, on the Nek, because
they will think you are to cover our getting away.
They will shell the Nek. They will miss. You
will then ride away. All the rooineks will come
after you, hot and in a hurry—perhaps, even,
with their cannon. They will pass our fires and
our fresh horse-dung. They will come here as
their scoots came. They will see the plain so
full of our dust. They will say, ' The scoots
spoke truth. It is a full retreat.' *Then* we up
there on the rocks will shoot, and it will be like
the fight at Stormberg in daytime. Do you
understand *now*?"

Those of the commando directly interested lit
new pipes and discussed the matter in detail till
midnight.

Next morning the operations began with, if
one may borrow the language of some official de-
spatches—"the precision of well-oiled machinery."

The helio-station reported the dust of the
wagons and the movements of armed men in
full flight across the plain beyond the kopjes. A
Colonel, newly appointed from England, by
reason of his seniority, sent forth a dozen Mounted
Infantry under command of a Captain. Till
a month ago they had been drilled by a cavalry

ınstructor, who taught them "shock" tactics to the music of trumpets. They knew how to advance in echelon of squadrons, by cat's cradle of troops, in quarter column of stable-litter, how to trot, to gallop, and above all to charge. They knew how to sit their horses unremittingly, so that at the day's end they might boast how many hours they had been in the saddle without relief, and they learned to rejoice in the clatter and stamp of a troop moving as such, and therefore audible five miles away.

They trotted out two and two along the farm road, that trailed lazily through the wind-driven dust; across the half-dried ford to a nek between low stony hills leading into the debatable land. (Vrooman of Emmaus from his neatly bushed hole noted that one man carried a sporting Lee-Enfield rifle with a short fore-end. Vrooman of Emmaus argued that the owner of it was the officer to be killed on his return, and went to sleep.) They saw nothing except a small flock of sheep and a Kaffir herdsman who spoke broken English with curious fluency. He had heard that the Boers had decided to retreat on account of their sick and wounded. The Captain in charge of the detachment turned to look at the helio-station four miles away. "Hurry up," said the dazzling flash. "Retreat apparently continues, but suggest you make sure. Quick."

" Ye-es," said the Captain, a shade bitterly, as he wiped the sweat from a sun-skinned nose. " You want me to come back and report all clear. If anything happens it will be my fault. If they get away it will be my fault for disregarding the signal. I love officers who suggest and advise, and want to make their reputations in twenty minutes."

" 'Don't see much 'ere, sir," said the sergeant, scanning the bare cup of the hollow where a dust-devil danced alone.

" No? We'll go on."

" If we get among these steep 'ills we lose touch of the 'elio."

" Very likely. Trot."

The rounded mounds grew to spiked kopjes, heart-breaking to climb under a hot sun at four thousand feet above sea level. This is where the scouts found their spurs peculiarly useful.

Jan van Staden had thoughtfully allowed the invading force a front of two rifle-shots or four thousand yards, and they kept a thousand yards within his estimate. Ten men strung over two miles feel that they have explored all the round earth.

They saw stony slopes combing over in scrub, narrow valleys clothed with stone, low ridges of splintered stone, and tufts of brittle-stemmed bush. An irritating wind, split up by many rocky barriers, cuffed them over the ears and slapped them in the face at every turn.   They came upon an abandoned camp fire, a little fresh horse-dung, and an empty ammunition-box splintered up for firewood, an old boot, and a stale bandage.

A few hundred yards farther along the road a battered Mauser had been thrown into a bush. The glimmer of its barrel drew the scouts from the hillside, and here the road after passing between two flat-topped kopjes entered a valley nearly half a mile wide, rose slightly, and over the nek of a ridge gave clear view across the windy plain northward.

"They're on the dead run, for sure," said a trooper.   "Here's their fires and their litter and their guns, and that's where they're bolting to."   He pointed over the ridge to the bellying dust cloud a mile long.   A vulture high over-head flickered down, steadied herself, and hung motionless.

"See!" said Jan van Staden from the rocks above the road, to his waiting commando.   "It turns like a well-oiled wheel.   They look where they need not look, but *here*, where they should look on both sides, they look at our retreat— straight before them.   It is tempting our people too much.   I pray God no one will shoot them."

"That's about the size of it," said the Captain, rubbing the dust from his binoculars.   "Boers

on the run. I expect they find their main line
of retreat to the north is threatened. We'll get
back and tell the camp." He wheeled his pony
and his eye traversed the flat-topped kopje
commanding the road. The stones at its edge
seemed to be piled with less than Nature's
carelessness.

" That 'ud be a dashed ugly place if it were
occupied—and that other one, too. Those rocks
aren't five hundred yards from the road, either
of 'em. Hold on, sergeant, I'll light a pipe."
He bent over the bowl, and above his lighted
match squinted at the kopje. A stone, a small
roundish brown boulder on the lip of another
one, seemed to move very slightly. The short
hairs of his neck grated his collar. " I'll have
another squint at their retreat," he cried to the
sergeant, astonished at the steadiness of his own
voice. He swept the plain, and, wheeling, let
the glass rest for a moment on the kopje's top.
One cranny between the rocks was pinkish,
where blue sky should have shown. His men,
dotted down the valley, sat heavily on their horses
—it never occurred to them to dismount. He
could hear the squeak of the leathers as a man
shifted. An impatient gust blew through the
valley and rattled the bushes. On all sides the
expectant hills stood still under the pale blue.

" And we passed within a quarter of a mile

of 'em! We're done!" The thumping heart slowed down, and the Captain began to think clearly—so clearly that the thoughts seemed solid things. " It's Pretoria gaol for us all. Perhaps that man's only a look-out, though. We'll have to bolt! And I led 'em into it! . . . You fool," said his other self, above the beat of the blood in his eardrums. " If they could snipe you all from up there, why haven't they begun already? Because you're the bait for the rest of the attack. They don't want you *now*. You're to go back and bring up the others to be killed. Go back! Don't detach a man or they'll suspect. Go back all together. Tell the sergeant you're going. Some of them up there will understand English. Tell it aloud! Then back you go with the news—the real news."

" The country's all clear, sergeant," he shouted. " We'll go back and tell the Colonel." With an idiotic giggle he added, " It's a good road for guns, don't you think?"

" Hear you that?" said Jan van Staden, gripping a burgher's arm. " God is on our side to-day. They *will* bring their little cannons after all!"

" Go easy. No good bucketing the horses to pieces. We'll need 'em for the pursuit later," said the Captain. " Hullo, there's a vulture! How far would you make him?"

E

" Can't tell, sir, in this dry air."

The bird swooped towards the second flat-topped kopje, but suddenly shivered sideways, and wheeled off again, followed intently by the Captain's glance.

" And that kopje's simply full of 'em, too," he said, flushing. " Perfectly confident they are, that we'd take this road—and then they'll scupper the whole boiling of us! They'll let us through to fetch up the others. But I mustn't let 'em know we know. By Jove, they do *not* think much of us! 'Don't blame 'em."

The cunning of the trap did not impress him until later.

Down the track jolted a dozen well-equipped men, laughing and talking—a mark to make a pious burgher's mouth water. Thrice had their Captain explicitly said that they were to march easy, so a trooper began to hum a tune that he had picked up in Capetown streets:

> Vat jou goet en trek, Ferriera,
> Vat jou goet en trek;
> Jannie met de hoepel bein, Ferriera,
> Jannie met de hoepel bein!

Then with a whistle:

> Zwaar draa—-alle en de ein kant—

The Captain, thinking furiously, found his mind turn to a camp in the Karroo, months before; an engine that had halted in that waste,

and a woman with brown hair, early grizzled—
an extraordinary woman. . . . Yes, but as soon
as they had dropped the flat-topped kopje behind
its neighbour he must hurry back and report.
. . . A woman with grey eyes and black eye-
lashes. . . . The Boers would probably be
massed on those two kopjes. How soon dare
he break into a canter? . . . A woman with a
queer cadence in her speech. . . . It was not
more than five miles home by the straight road—
" *Even when we were children we learned not
to go back by the way we had come.*"

The sentence came back to him, self-shouted,
so clearly that he almost turned to see if the
scouts had heard. The two flat-topped kopjes
behind him were covered by a long ridge. The
camp lay due south. He had only to follow the
road to the Nek—a notch, unscouted as he re-
called now, between the two hills.

He wheeled his men up a long valley.

" Excuse me, sir, that ain't our road!" said the
sergeant. " Once we get over this rise, straight
on, we come into direct touch with the 'elio, on
that flat bit o' road there they 'elioed us goin' out."

" But we aren't going to get in touch with
them just now. Come along, and come quick."

" What's the meaning of this?" said a private
in the rear. " What's 'e doin' this detour for?
We sha'n't get in for hours an' hours."

" Come on, men.   Flog a canter out of your brutes, somehow," the Captain called back.

For two throat-parched hours he held west by south, away from the Nek, puzzling over a compass already demented by the ironstone in the hills, and then turned south-east through an eruption of low hills that ran far into the re-entering bend of the river that circled the left bank of the camp.

Eight miles to eastward that student from Stellenbosch had wriggled out on the rocks above the Nek to have a word with Vrooman of Emmaus. The bottom seemed to have dropped out of at least one portion of their programme; for the scouting party were not to be seen.

" Jan is a clever man," he said to his companion, " but he does not think that even rooineks may learn.   Perhaps those scouts will have seen Jan's commando, and perhaps they will come back to warn the rooineks.   That is why I think he should have shot them *before* they came to the Nek, and made quite sure that only one or two got away.   It would have made the English angry, and they would have come out across the open in hundreds to be shot.   Then when we ran away they would have come after us without thinking.   If you can make the English hurry, they never think.   Jan is wrong this time."

" Lie down, and pray you have not shown

yourself to their helio-station," growled Vrooman
of Emmaus. "You throw with your arms and
kick with your legs like a rooinek. When we
get back I will tell Jan and he will sjambok you.
All will yet come right. They will go and warn
the rest, and the rest will hurry out by this very nek.
Then we can shoot. Now you lie still and wait."

"'Ere's a rummy picnic. We left camp,
as it were, by the front door. 'E 'as given us
a giddy-go-round, an' no mistake," said a dripping
private as he dismounted behind the infantry
lines.

"Did you see our helio?" This was the
Colonel, hot from racing down from the helio-
station. "There were a lot of Boers waiting
for you on the Nek. We saw 'em. We tried
to get at you with the helio, and tell you we were
coming out to help you. Then we saw you
didn't come over that flat bit of road where we
had signalled you going out, and we wondered
why. We didn't hear any shots."

"I turned off, sir, and came in by another
road," said the Captain.

"By another road!" The Colonel lifted his
eyebrows. "Perhaps you're not aware, sir, that
the Boers have been in full retreat for the last
three hours, and that those men on the Nek
were simply a rear-guard put out to delay us for
a little. We could see that much from here.

Your duty, sir, was to have taken them in the rear, and then we could have brushed them aside. The Boer retreat has been going on all morning, sir—all morning. You were despatched to see the front clear and to return at once. The whole camp has been under arms for three hours; and instead of doing your work you wander all about Africa with your scouts to avoid a handful of skulking Boers! You should have sent a man back at once—you should have—— "

The Captain got off his horse stiffly.

"As a matter of fact," said he, "I didn't know for sure that there were any Boers on the Nek, but I went round it in case it was so. But I *do* know that the kopjes beyond the Nek are simply crawling with Boers."

"Nonsense. We can see the whole lot of 'em retreating out yonder."

"Of course you can. That's part of their game, sir. I saw 'em lying on the top of a couple of kopjes commanding the road, where it goes into the plain on the far side. They let us come in to see, and they let us go out to report the country clear and bring you up. Now they are waiting for *you*. The whole thing is a trap."

"D'you expect any officer of my experience to believe that?"

"As you please, sir," said the Captain hopelessly. "My responsibility ends with my report."

AN UNQUALIFIED PILOT

AN UNQUALIFIED PILOT

This tale is founded on something that happened a good many years ago in the Port of Calcutta, before wireless telegraphy was used on ships, and men and boys were less easy to catch when once they were in a ship. It is not meant to show that anybody who thinks he would like to become eminent in his business can do so at a moment's notice; but it proves the old saying that if you want anything badly enough and are willing to pay the price for it, you generally get it. If you don't get what you want it is a sign either that you did not seriously want it, or that you tried to bargain over the price.

ALMOST any pilot will tell you that his work is much more difficult than you imagine; but the Pilots of the Hugli know that they have one hundred miles of the most dangerous river on earth running through their hands—the Hugli between Calcutta and the Bay of Bengal—and they say nothing. Their service is picked and sifted as carefully as the bench of the Supreme Court, for a judge can only hang the wrong man, or pass a bad law; but a careless pilot can lose a ten-thousand-ton ship with crew and cargo in less time than it takes to reverse her engines.

There is very little chance of anything getting

57

off again when once she touches in the furious Hugli current, loaded with all the fat silt of the fields of Bengal, where the soundings change two feet between tides, and new channels make and unmake themselves in one rainy season. Men have fought the Hugli for two hundred years, till now the river owns a huge building, with drawing, survey, and telegraph departments, devoted to its private service, as well as a body of wardens, who are called the Port Commissioners.

They and their officers govern everything that floats from the Hugli Bridge to the last buoy at Pilots Ridge, one hundred and forty miles away, far out in the Bay of Bengal, where the steamers first pick up the pilots from the pilot brig.

A Hugli pilot does not kindly bring papers aboard for the passengers, or scramble up the ship's side by wet, swaying rope-ladders. He arrives in his best clothes, with a native servant or an assistant pilot to wait on him, and he behaves as a man should who can earn two or three thousand pounds a year after twenty years' apprenticeship. He has beautiful rooms in the Port Office at Calcutta, and generally keeps himself to the society of his own profession, for though the telegraph reports the more important soundings of the river daily, there is much to be learned from brother pilots between each trip.

Some million tons of shipping must find their way to and from Calcutta each twelvemonth, and unless the Hugli were watched as closely as his keeper watches an elephant, there is a fear that it might silt up, as it has silted up round the old Dutch and Portuguese ports twenty and thirty miles behind Calcutta.

So the Port Office sounds and scours and dredges the river, and builds spurs and devices for coaxing currents, and labels all the buoys with their proper letters, and attends to the semaphores and the lights and the drum, ball and cone storm signals; and the pilots of the Hugli do the rest; but, in spite of all care and the very best attention, the Hugli swallows her ship or two every year. Even the coming of wireless telegraphy does not spoil her appetite.

When Martin Trevor had waited on the river from his boyhood; when he had risen to be a Senior Pilot, entitled to bring up to Calcutta the very biggest ships; when he had thought and talked of nothing but Hugli pilotage all his life to nobody except Hugli pilots, he was exceedingly surprised and indignant that his only son should decide to follow his father's profession. Mrs. Trevor had died when the boy was a child, and as he grew older, Trevor, in the intervals of his business, noticed that the lad was very often by the river-side—no place, he said, for a nice boy.

But, as he was not often at home, and as the aunt who looked after Jim naturally could not follow him to his chosen haunts, and as Jim had not the faintest intention of giving up old friends there, nothing but ineffectual growls came of the remark. Later, when Trevor once asked him if he could make anything out of the shipping on the water, Jim replied by reeling off the list of all the house-flags in sight at the moorings, together with supplementary information about their tonnage and captains.

" You'll come to a bad end, Jim," said Trevor. " Boys of your age haven't any business to waste their time on these things."

" Oh, Pedro at the Sailors' Home says you can't begin too early."

" At what, please?"

" Piloting. I'm nearly fourteen now, and— and I know where most of the shipping in the river is, and I know what there was yesterday over the Mayapur Bar, and I've been down to Diamond Harbour—oh, a hundred times already, and I've——"

" You'll go to school, son, and learn what they teach you, and you'll turn out something better than a pilot," said his father, who wanted Jim to enter the Subordinate Civil Service, but he might just as well have told a shovel-nosed porpoise of the river to come ashore and begin life as a hen. Jim held his tongue; he noticed that all the best pilots in the Port Office did that; and devoted his young attention and all his spare time to the River he loved. He had seen the nice young gentlemen in the Subordinate Civil Service, and he called them a rude native name for " clerks."

He became as well known as the Bankshall itself; and the Port Police let him inspect their launches, and the tug-boat captains had always a place for him at their tables, and the mates of the big steam dredgers used to show him how the machinery worked, and there were certain native row-boats which Jim practically owned; and he extended his patronage to the railway that runs to Diamond Harbour, forty miles down the river. In the old days nearly all the East India Company's ships used to discharge at Diamond Harbour, on account of the shoals above, but now ships go straight up to Calcutta, and they have only some moorings for vessels in distress there, and a telegraph service, and a harbour-master, who was one of Jim's most intimate friends.

He would sit in the Office listening to the soundings of the shoals as they were reported every day, and attending to the movements of the steamers up and down (Jim always felt he had lost something irretrievable if a boat got in or out of the river without his knowing of it), and when the big liners with their rows of blazing portholes tied up in Diamond Harbour for the night, Jim would row from one ship to the other through the sticky hot air and the buzzing mosquitoes and listen respectfully as the pilots conferred together about the habits of steamers.

Once, for a treat, his father took him down clear out to the Sandheads and the pilot brig there, and Jim was happily sea-sick as she tossed and pitched in the Bay. The cream of life, though, was coming up in a tug or a police boat from Diamond Harbour to Calcutta, over the " James and Mary," those terrible sands christened after a royal ship that they sunk two hundred years before. They are made by two rivers that enter the Hugli six miles apart and throw their own silt across the silt of the main stream, so that with each turn of the weather and tide the sands shift and change under water like clouds in the sky. It was here (the tales sound much worse when they are told in the rush and growl of the muddy waters) that the *Countess of Stirling*, fifteen hundred tons, touched and capsized in ten minutes, and a two-thousand-ton steamer in two, and a pilgrim ship in five, and another steamer literally in one instant, holding down her men with the masts and shrouds as she lashed over. When a ship touches on the " James and Mary," the river knocks her down and buries her, and the sands quiver all around her and reach out under water and take new shapes over the corpse.

Young Jim would lie up in the bows of the tug and watch the straining buoys kick and choke in the coffee-coloured current, while the sema-phores and flags signalled from the bank how much water there was in the channel, till he learned that men who deal with men can afford to be careless, on the chance of their fellows being like them; but men who deal with things dare not relax for an instant. " And that's the very reason," old McEwan said to him once, " that the ' James and Mary ' is the safest part of the river," and he shoved the big black *Bandoorah*, that draws twenty-five feet, through the Eastern Gat, with a turban of white foam wrapped round her forefoot and her screw beating as steadily as his own heart.

If Jim could not get away to the river there was always the big, cool Port Office, where the soundings were worked out and the maps drawn; or the Pilots' room, where he could lie in a long chair and listen quietly to the talk about the Hugli; and there was the library, where if you had money you could buy charts and books of direc-tions against the time that you would actually have to steam over the places themselves.   It was exceedingly hard for Jim to hold the list of Jewish Kings in his head, and he was more than un-certain as to the end of the verb *audio* if you followed it far enough down the page, but he could keep the soundings of three channels distinct in his head, and, what is more confusing, the changes in the buoys from " Garden Reach " down to Saugor, as well as the greater part of the *Calcutta Telegraph*, the only paper he ever read.

Unluckily, you cannot peruse about the Hugli without money, even though you are the son of the best-known pilot on the river, and as soon as Trevor understood how his son was spending his time, he cut down his pocket money, of which Jim had a very generous allowance. In his extremity he took counsel with Pedro, the plum-coloured mulatto at the Sailors' Home, and Pedro was a bad, designing man. He introduced Jim to a Chinaman in Muchuatollah, an unpleasing place in itself, and the Chinaman, who answered to the name of Erh-Tze, when he was not smoking opium, talked business in pigeon-English to Jim for an hour. Every bit of that business from first to last was flying in the face of every law on the river, but it interested Jim.

" S'pose you takee. Can do? " Erh-Tze said at last.

Jim considered his chances. A junk, he knew, would draw about eleven feet and the regular fee for a qualified pilot, outward to the Sandheads, would be two hundred rupees. On the one hand he was not qualified, so he dared not ask more than half. *But*, on the other hand, he was fully certain of the thrashing of his life from his father for piloting without license, let alone what the Port Authorities might do to him. So he asked one hundred and seventy-five rupees, and Erh-Tze beat him down to a hundred and twenty. The cargo of his junk was worth anything from seventy to a hundred and fifty thousand rupees, some of which he was getting as enormous freight on the coffins of thirty or forty dead Chinamen, whom he was taking to be buried in their native country.

Rich Chinamen will pay fancy prices for this service, and they have a superstition that the iron of steamships is bad for the spiritual health of their dead. Erh-Tze's junk had crept up from Singapore, *via* Penang and Rangoon, to Calcutta, where Erh-Tze had been staggered by the Pilot dues. This time he was going out at a reduction with Jim, who, as Pedro kept telling him, was just as good as a pilot, and a heap cheaper.

Jim knew something of the manners of junks, but he was not prepared, when he went down that night with his charts, for the confusion of cargo and coolies and coffins and clay-cooking places, and other things that littered her decks. He had sense enough to haul the rudder up a few feet, for he knew that a junk's rudder goes far below the bottom, and he allowed a foot extra to

F

Erh-Tze's estimate of the junk's depth. Then they staggered out into midstream very early, and never had the city of his birth looked so beautiful as when he feared he would not come back to see it. Going down " Garden Reach " he discovered that the junk would answer to her helm if you put it over far enough, and that she had a fair, though Chinese, notion of sailing. He took charge of the tiller by stationing three Chinese on each side of it, and standing a little forward, gathered their pigtails into his hands, three right and three left, as though they had been the yoke lines of a row-boat. Erh-Tze almost smiled at this; he felt he was getting good care for his money and took a neat little polished bamboo to keep the men attentive, for he said this was no time to teach the crew pigeon-English. The more way they could get on the junk the better would she steer, and as soon as he felt a little confidence in her, Jim ordered the stiff, rustling sails to be hauled up tighter and tighter. He did not know their names—at least any name that would be likely to interest a Chinaman—but Erh-Tze had not banged about the waters of the Malay Archipelago all his life for nothing. He rolled forward with his bamboo, and the things rose like Eastern incantations.

Early as they were on the river, a big American oil (but they called it kerosene in those days) ship was ahead of them in tow, and when Jim saw her through the lifted mist he was thankful. She would draw all of seventeen feet, and if he could steer by her they would be safe. It is easier to scurry up and down the "James and Mary" in a police-boat that some one else is handling than to cram a hard-mouthed old junk across the same sands alone, with the certainty of a thrashing if you come out alive.

Jim glued his eyes to the American, and saw that at Fultah she dropped her tug and stood down the river under sail. He all but whooped aloud, for he knew that the number of pilots who preferred to work a ship through the "James and Mary" was strictly limited. " If it isn't Father, it's Dearsley," said Jim, " and Dearsley went down yesterday with the *Bancoora*, so it's Father. If I'd gone home last night instead of going to Pedro, I'd have met him. He must have got his ship quick, but—Father *is* a very quick man." Then Jim reflected that they kept a piece of knotted rope on the pilot brig that stung like a wasp; but this thought he dismissed as beneath the dignity of an officiating pilot, who needed only to nod his head to set Erh-Tze's bamboo to work.

As the American came round, just before the Fultah Sands, Jim raked her with his spy-glass, and saw his father on the poop, an unlighted cigar between his teeth. That cigar, Jim knew, would be smoked on the other side of the "James and Mary," and Jim felt so entirely safe and happy that he lit a cigar on his own account. This kind of piloting was child's play. His father could not make a mistake if he tried; and Jim, with his six obedient pigtails in his two hands, had leisure to admire the perfect style in which the American was handled—how she would point her bowsprit jeeringly at a hidden bank, as much as to say, "Not to-day, thank you, dear," and bow down lovingly to a buoy as much as to say, "*You*'re a gentleman, at any rate," and come round sharp on her heel with a flutter and a rustle, and a slow, steady swing something like a well-dressed woman staring all round the theatre through opera-glasses.

It was hard work to keep the junk near her, though Erh-Tze set everything that was by any means settable, and used his bamboo most generously. When they were nearly under her counter, and a little to her left, Jim, hidden behind a sail, would feel warm and happy all over, thinking of the thousand nautical and piloting things that he knew. When they fell more than half a mile behind, he was cold and miserable thinking of all the million things he did not know or was not quite sure of. And so they went down, Jim steering by his father, turn for turn, over the Mayapur Bar, with the semaphores on each bank duly signalling the depth of water, through the

Western Gat, and round Makoaputti Lumps, and in and out of twenty places, each more exciting than the last, and Jim nearly pulled the six pigtails out for pure joy when the last of the "James and Mary" had gone astern, and they were walking through Diamond Harbour.

From there to the mouth of the Hugli things are not so bad—at least, that was what Jim thought, and held on till the swell from the Bay of Bengal made the old junk heave and snort, and the river broadened into the inland sea, with islands only a foot or two high scattered about it. The American walked away from the junk as soon as they were beyond Kedgeree, and the night came on and the river looked very big and desolate, so Jim promptly anchored somewhere in grey water, with the Saugor Light away off toward the east. He had a great respect for the Hugli to the last yard of her, and had no desire whatever to find himself on the Gasper Sand or any other little shoal. Erh-Tze and the crew highly approved of this piece of seamanship. They set no watch, lit no lights, and at once went to sleep.

Jim lay down between a red-and-black lacquer coffin and a little live pig in a basket. As soon as it was light he began studying his chart of the Hugli mouth, and trying to find out where in the river he might be. He decided to be on the safe side and wait for another sailing-ship and follow her out. So he made an enormous breakfast of rice and boiled fish, while Erh-Tze lit fire-crackers and burned gilt paper to the Joss who had saved them so far. Then they heaved up their rough-and-tumble anchor, and made after a big, fat, iron four-masted sailing-ship, heavy as a hay-wain.

The junk, which was really a very weatherly boat, and might have begun life as a private pirate in Annam forty years before, followed under easy sail; for the four-master would run no risks. She was in old McEwan's hands, and she waddled about like a broody hen, giving each shoal wide allowances. All this happened near the outer Floating Light, some hundred and twenty miles from Calcutta, and apparently in the open sea.

Jim knew old McEwan's appetite, and often heard him pride himself on getting his ship to the pilot brig close upon meal hours, so he argued that if the pilot brig was get-at-able (and Jim himself had not the ghost of a notion where she would lie), McEwan would find her before one o'clock.

It was a blazing hot day, and McEwan fidgeted the four-master down to " Pilots Ridge " with what little wind remained, and sure enough there lay the pilot brig, and Jim felt shivers up his back as Erh-Tze paid him his hundred and twenty rupees and he went overside in the junk's

one crazy dinghy. McEwan was leaving the
four-master in a long, slashing whale-boat that
looked very spruce and pretty, and Jim could
see that there was a certain amount of excitement
among the pilots on the brig. There was his
father too. The ragged Chinese boatmen gave
way in a most ragged fashion, and Jim felt very
unwashen and disreputable when he heard the
click of McEwan's oars alongside, and McEwan
saying, " James Trevor, I'll trouble you to lay
alongside me."

Jim obeyed, and from the corner of one eye
watched McEwan's angry whiskers stand up
all round his face, which turned purple.

" An' how is it you break the regulations o'
the Porrt o' Calcutta? Are ye aware o' the
penalties and impreesonments ye've laid yourself
open to?" McEwan began.

Jim said nothing. There was not very much
to say just then; and McEwan roared aloud:
" Man, ye've perrsonated a Hugli pilot, an' that's
as much as to say ye've perrsonated *ME!* What
did yon heathen give ye for honorarium?"

" 'Hundred and twenty," said Jim.

" An' by what manner o' means did ye get
through the ' James and Mary '?"

" Father," was the answer. " He went down
the same tide and I—we—steered by him."

McEwan whistled and choked, perhaps it

was with anger. " Ye've made a stalkin'-horse o' your father, then? Jim, laddie, he'll make an example o' you."

The boat hooked on to the brig's chains, and McEwan said, as he set foot on deck before Jim could speak, " Yon's an enterprising cub o' yours, Trevor. Ye'd better enter him in the regular business, or one o' these fine days he'll be acting as pilot before he's qualified, and sinkin' junks in the fairway. He fetched yon junk down last night. If ye've no other designs I'm thinkin' I'll take him as my cub, for there's no denying he's a resourceful lad—for all he's an unlicked whelp."

" That," said Trevor, reaching for Jim's left ear, " is something we can remedy," and he led him below.

The little knotted rope that they keep for general purposes on the pilot brig did its duty, but when it was all over Jim was unlicked no longer. He was McEwan's property to be registered under the laws of the Port of Calcutta, and a week later, when the *Ellora* came along, he bundled over the pilot brig's side with McEwan's enamelled leather hand-bag and a roll of charts and a little bag of his own, and he dropped into the sternsheets of the pilot gig with a very creditable imitation of McEwan's slow, swaying sit-down and hump of the shoulders.

THE JUNK AND DHOW

ONCE a pair of savages found a stranded tree.
   (*One-piecee stick-pidgin—two-piecee man.*
Straddle-um—paddle-um—push-um off to sea.
   That way Foleign Devil-boat began.[1])
But before, and before, and ever so long before
   Any shape of sailing-craft was known,
The Junk and Dhow had a stern and a bow,
   And a mast and a sail of their own—alone, alone!
   As they crashed across the Oceans on their own!

Once there was a pirate-ship, being blown ashore—
   (*Plitty soon pilum up, s'posee no can tack.*
Seven-piecee stlong man pullum sta'boa'd oar.
   That way bling her head alound and sail-o back.)
But before, and before, and ever so long before
   Grand Commander Noah took the wheel,
The Junk and the Dhow, though they look like anyhow,
   Had rudders reaching deep below their keel—akeel—
      akeel!
   As they laid the Eastern Seas beneath their keel!

Once there was a galliot yawing in a tide.
   (*Too much foolee side-slip.   How can stop?*
Man catchee tea-box lid—lasha longaside.
   That way make her plenty glip and sail first-chop.)
But before, and before, and ever so long before
   Any such contrivances were used,

   [1] Remember, the Chinaman generally says " l " for " r."

73

The whole Confucian sea-board had standardized the lee-
board,
  And hauled it up or dropped it as they choosed—or
    chose—or choosed!
  According to the weather, when they cruised!

Once there was a caravel in a beam-sea roll—
  (*Cargo shiftee—alla dliftee—no can livee long.*
S'posum' nail-o boa'd acloss—makee ploper hol'?
  That way, cargo sittum still, an' ship mo' stlong.)
But before, and before, and ever so long before
  Any square-rigged vessel hove in sight
The Canton deep-sea craft carried bulkheads fore and aft,
  And took good care to keep 'em water-tight—atite—
    atite!
  From Amboyna to the Great Australian Bight!

Once there was a sailor-man singing just this way—
  (*Too muchee yowl-o, sickum best flend!*
Singee all-same pullee lope—haul and belay.
  Hully up and coilum down an'—bite off end!)
But before, and before, and ever so long before
  Any sort of chanty crossed our lips,
The Junk and the Dhow, though they look like anyhow,
  Were the Mother and the Father of all Ships—ahoy!—
    aships!
  And of half the new inventions in our Ships!
  From Tarifa to Formosa of our Ships!
    From Socotra to Sel*an*khor of the windlass and the
      anchor,
  And the Navigators' Compass on our Ships—ahoy!—
    our Ships!
(*O, hully up and coilum down and bite off end!*)

HIS GIFT

HIS GIFT

His Scoutmaster and his comrades, who disagreed on several points, were united in one conviction—that William Glasse Sawyer was, without exception, the most unprofitable person, not merely in the Pelican Troop, who lived in the wilderness of the 47th Postal District, London, S.E., but in the whole body of Boy Scouts throughout the world.

No one, except a ferocious uncle who was also a French-polisher, seemed responsible for his beginnings. There was a legend that he had been entered as a Wolf-Cub at the age of eight, under Miss Doughty, whom the uncle had either bribed or terrorized to accept him; and that after six months Miss Doughty confessed that she could make nothing of him and retired to teach school in the Yorkshire moors. There is also a red-headed ex-cub of that troop (he is now in a shipping-office) who asserts proudly that he used to bite William Glasse Sawyer on the leg in the hope of waking him up, and takes most of the credit for William's present success. But when

William moved into the larger life of the Pelicans, who were gay birds, he was not what you might call alert. In shape he resembled the ace of diamonds; in colour he was an oily sallow.

He could accomplish nothing that required one glimmer of reason, thought or common-sense. He cleaned himself only under bitter compulsion; he lost his bearings equally in town or country after a five-minutes' stroll. He could track nothing smaller than a tram-car on a single line, and that only if there were no traffic. He could neither hammer a nail, carry an order, tie a knot, light a fire, notice any natural object, except food, or use any edged tool except a table-knife. To crown all, his innumerable errors and omissions were not even funny.

But it is an old law of human nature that if you hold to one known course of conduct—good or evil—you end by becoming an institution; and when he was fifteen or thereabouts William achieved that position. The Pelicans gradually took pride in the notorious fact that they possessed the only Sealed Pattern, Mark A, Ass—an unique jewel, so to speak, of Absolute, Unalterable Incapacity. The poet of a neighbouring troop used to write verses about him, and recite them from public places, such as the tops of passing trams. William made no comment, but wrapped himself up in long silences that he seldom broke till the juniors of the Troop (the elders had given it up long before) tried to do him good turns with their scout-staves.

In private life he assisted his uncle at the mystery of French-polishing, which, he said, was " boiling up things in pots and rubbing down bits of wood." The boiling-up, he said, he did not mind so much. The rubbing down he hated. Once, too, he volunteered that his uncle and only relative had been in the Navy, and " did not like to be played with "; and the vision of William playing with any human being upset even his Scoutmaster.

Now it happened, upon a certain summer that was really a summer with heat to it, the Pelicans had been lent a dream of a summer camp in a dream of a park, which offered opportunities for every form of diversion, including bridging muddy-banked streams, and unlimited cutting into young alders and undergrowth at large. A convenient village lay just outside the Park wall, and the ferny slopes round the camp were rich in rabbits, not to mention hedgehogs and other fascinating vermin. It was reached—Mr. Hale their Scoutmaster saw to that—after two days' hard labour, with the Troop push-cart, along sunny roads.

William's share in the affair was—what it had always been. First he lost most of his kit; next

his uncle talked to him after the fashion of the
Navy of '96 before refitting him; thirdly he went
lame behind the push-cart by reason of a stone in
his shoe, and on arrival in camp dropped—not
for the first, second or third time—into his un-
honoured office as Camp Orderly, and was placed
at the disposal of The Prawn, whose light blue
eyes stuck out from his freckled face, and whose
long narrow chest was covered with badges.
From that point on, the procedure was as usual.
Once again did The Prawn assure his Scoutmaster
that he would take enormous care of William and
give him work suited to his capacity and intelligence. Once again did William grunt and
wriggle at the news, and once again in the silence
of the deserted camp next morning, while the rest
of the Pelicans were joyously mucking themselves
up to their young bills at bridging brooks, did he
bow his neck to The Prawn's many orders. For
The Prawn was a born organizer. He set
William to unpack the push-cart and then to
neatly and exactly replace all parcels, bags, tins,
and boxes. He despatched him thrice in the
forenoon across the hot Park to fetch water from a
distant well equipped with a stiff-necked windlass
and a split handle that pinched William's fat
palms. He bade him collect sticks, thorny for
choice, out of the flanks of a hedge full of ripe
nettles against which Scout uniforms offer small

protection. He then made him lay them in the camp cooking-place, carefully rejecting the green ones, for most sticks were alike to William; and when everything else failed, he set him to pick up stray papers and rubbish the length and breadth of the camp. All that while, he not only chased him with comments but expected that William would show gratitude to him for forming his young mind.

" 'Tisn't every one 'ud take this amount o' trouble with you, Mug," said The Prawn virtuously, when even his energetic soul could make no further work for his vassal. " Now you open that bully-beef tin and we'll have something to eat, and then you're off duty—for a bit. I shall try my hand at a little camp-cooking."

William found the tin—at the very bottom, of course, of the push-cart; cut himself generously over the knuckles in opening it (till The Prawn showed him how this should be done), and in due course, being full of bread and bully, withdrew towards a grateful clump of high fern that he had had his eye on for some time, wriggled deep into it, and on a little rabbit-browsed clearing of turf, stretched out and slept the sleep of the weary who have been up and under strict orders since six A.M. Till that hour of that day, be it remembered, William had given no proof either of intelligence or initiative in any direction.

G

He waked, slowly as was his habit, and noticed that the shadows were stretching a little, even as he stretched himself. Then he heard The Prawn clanking pot-lids, between soft bursts of song. William sniffed. The Prawn was cooking—was probably qualifying for something or other; The Prawn did nothing but qualify for badges. On reflection William discovered that he loved The Prawn even less this camp than the last, or the one before that. Then he heard the voice of a stranger.

"Yes," was The Prawn's reply. "I'm in charge of the camp. Would you like to look at it, sir?"

"'Seen 'em—seen heaps of 'em," said the unknown. "My son was in 'em once—Buffaloes, out Hendon-way. What are *you*?"

"Well, just now I'm a sort of temporary Cook," said The Prawn, whose manners were far better than William's.

"Temp'ry! Temp'ry!" the stranger puffed. "Can't be a temp'ry cook any more'n you can be a temp'ry Parson. Not so much. Cookin's cookin'! Let's see *your* notions of cookin'."

William had never heard any one address The Prawn in these tones, and somehow it cheered him. In the silence that followed he turned on his face and wriggled unostentatiously through the fern, as a Scout should, till he could see that bold

man without attracting The Prawn's notice.   And
this, too, was the first time that William had ever
profited by the instruction of his Scoutmaster or
the example of his comrades.

Heavenly sights rewarded him.   The Prawn,
visibly ill at ease, was shifting from one sinewy leg
to the other, while an enormously fat little man
with a pointed grey beard and arms like the fins of
a fish investigated a couple of pots that hung on
properly crutched sticks over the small fire that
William had lighted in the cooking-place.   He
did not seem to approve of what he saw or smelt.
And yet it was the impeccable Prawn's own
cookery!

" Lor!" said he at last after more sniffs of contempt, as he replaced the lid.   " If you hot up
things in tins, *that* ain't cookery.   That's vittles
—mere vittles!   And the way you've set that pot
on, you're drawing all the nesty wood-smoke into
the water.   The spuds won't take much harm of
it, but you've ruined the meat.   That *is* meat,
ain't it?   Get me a fork."

William hugged himself.   The Prawn, looking exactly like his namesake well-boiled, fetched
a big fork.   The little man prodded into the pot.

" It's stew!" The Prawn explained, but his
voice shook.

" Lor! " said the man again.   " It's boilin'!
It's boilin'!   You don't boil when you stew, my

son; an' as for *this* "—up came a grey slab of
mutton—" there's no odds between this and
motor-tyres. Well! Well! As I was sayin'
———" He joined his hands behind his globular
back and shook his head in silence. After a
while, The Prawn tried to assert himself.

"Cookin' isn't my strong point," began The
Prawn, " but——"

" Pore boys! Pore boys!" the stranger solilo-
quized, looking straight in front of him. " *Pore*
little boys! Wicked, *I* call it. They don't ever
let you make bread, do they, my son?"

The Prawn said they generally bought their
bread at a shop.

" Ah! I'm a shopkeeper meself. Marsh,
the Baker here, is me. *Pore* boys! Well! Well!
. . . Though it's against me own interest to say
so, *I* think shops are wicked. They sell people
things out o' tins which save 'em trouble, an' fill
the 'ospitals with stummick-cases afterwards. An'
the muck that's sold for flour. . . ." His voice
faded away and he meditated again. "Well—well!
As I was sayin'—— Pore boys! *Pore* boys! I'm
glad you ain't askin' me to dinner. Good-bye."

He rolled away across the fern, leaving The
Prawn dumb behind him.

It seemed to William best to wriggle back in
his cover as far as he could, ere The Prawn should
call him to work again. He was not a Scout by

instinct, but his uncle had shown him that when
things went wrong in the world, some one generally passed it on to some one else.   Very soon he
heard his name called, acidly, several times.   He
crawled out from the far end of the fern-patch,
rubbing his eyes, and The Prawn re-enslaved him
on the spot.   For once in his life William was
alert and intelligent, but The Prawn paid him no
compliments, nor when the very muddy Pelicans
came back from the bridging did The Prawn refer
in any way to the visit of Mr. E. M. Marsh &
Son, Bakers and Confectioners in the village street
just outside the Park wall.   Nor, for that matter,
did he serve the Pelicans much besides tinned
meats for their evening meal.

   To say that William did not sleep a wink that
night would be what has been called " nature-
faking "; which is a sin.   His system demanded
at least nine hours' rest, but he lay awake for quite
twenty minutes, during which he thought in-
tensely, rapidly and joyously.   Had he been asked
he would have said that his thoughts dealt solely
with The Prawn and the judgment that had fallen
upon him;   but William was no psychologist.
He did not know that hate—raging hate against
a too-badged, too virtuous senior—had shot him
into a new world, exactly as the large blunt shell
is heaved through space and dropped into a
factory, a garden or a barracks by the charge

behind it. And, as the shell, which is but metal and mixed chemicals, needs the mere graze on the fuse to spread itself all over the landscape, so did his mind need but the touch of that hate to flare up and illuminate not only all his world, but his own way through it.

Next morning something sang in his ear that it was long since he had done good turns to any one except his uncle, who was slow to appreciate them. He would amend that error; and the more safely since The Prawn would be off all that day with the Troop on a tramp in the natural history line, and his place as Camp Warden and Provost Marshal would be filled by the placid and easy-going Walrus, whose proper name was Carpenter, who never tried for badges, but who could not see a rabbit without going after him. And the owner of the Park had given full leave to the Pelicans to slay by any means, except a gun, any rabbits they could. So William ingratiated himself with his Superior Officer as soon as the Pelicans had left. . . .

No, the excellent Carpenter did not see that he needed William by his side all day. He might take himself and his bruised foot pretty much where he chose. He went, and this new and active mind of his that he did not realize, accompanied him—straight up the path of duty which, poetry tells us, is so often the road to glory.

He began by cleaning himself and his kit at seven o'clock in the morning, long before the village shops were open. This he did near a postern gate with a crack in it, in the Park wall, commanding a limited but quite sufficient view of the establishment of E. M. Marsh & Son across the street. It was perfect weather, and about eight o'clock Mr. Marsh himself in his shirt-sleeves rolled out to enjoy it before he took down the shutters. Hardly had he shifted the first of them when a fattish Boy Scout with a flat face and a slight limp laid hold of the second and began to slide it towards him.

" Well, well!" said Mr. Marsh. " Ah! Your good turn, eh?"

" Yes," said William briefly.

" That's right! Handsomely now, handsomely," for the shutter was jamming in its groove. William knew from his uncle that " handsomely " meant slowly and with care. The shutter responded to the coaxing. The others followed.

" Belay!" said Mr. Marsh, wiping his forehead, for, like William, he perspired easily. When he turned round William had gone. The Movies had taught him, though he knew it not, the value of dramatic effect. He continued to watch Mr. Marsh through the crack in the postern—it was the little wooden door at the end of the right of way through the Park—and when, an hour or so later, Mr. Marsh came out of his shop and headed towards it, William retired backwards into the high fern and brambles. The manœuvre would have rejoiced Mr. Hale's heart, for generally William moved like an elephant with its young. He turned up, quite casually, when Mr. Marsh had puffed his way again into the empty camp. Carpenter was off in pursuit of rabbits, with a pocket full of fine picture-wire. It was the first time William had ever done the honours of any establishment. He came to attention and smiled.

"Well! Well!" Mr. Marsh nodded friend-lily. "What are *you*?"

"Camp-Guard," said William, improvising for the first time in his life. "Can I show you anything, sir?"

"No, thank'ee. My son was a Scout once. I've just come to look round at things. 'No one tryin' any cookin' to-day?"

"No, sir."

"'Bout's well. *Pore* boys! What you goin' to have for dinner? Tinned stuff?"

"I expect so, sir."

"D'you like it?"

"'Used to it." William rather approved of this round person who wasted no time on abstract ideas.

" *Pore* boys! Well! Well! It saves trouble
—for the present. Knots and splices in your
stummick afterwards—in 'ospital." Mr. Marsh
looked at the cold camp cooking-place and its
three big stones, and sniffed.

" Would you like it lit?" said William,
suddenly.

" What for?"

" To cook with."

" What d'*you* know about cookin'?" Mr.
Marsh's little eyes opened wide.

" Nothing, sir."

" What makes you think *I*'m a cook?"

" By the way you looked at our cooking-
place," the mendacious William answered. The
Prawn had always urged him to cultivate habits
of observation. They seemed easy—after you
had observed the things.

" Well! Well! Quite a young Sherlock,
you are. 'Don't think much o' *this*, though."
Mr. Marsh began to stoop to rearrange the open-
air hearth to his liking.

" Show me how and I'll do it," said William.

" Shove that stone a little more to the left then.
Steady—So! That'll do! Got any wood? No?
You slip across to the shop and ask them to give
you some small brush-stuff from the oven. Stop!
And my apron, too. Marsh is the name."

William left him chuckling wheezily. When

he returned Mr. Marsh clad himself in a long
white apron of office which showed so clearly that
Carpenter from far off returned at once.

"H'sh!   H'sh!" said Mr. Marsh before he
could speak. "You carry on with what you're
doing. Marsh is my name. My son was a
Scout once. Buffaloes—Hendon-way. It's all
right. Don't you grudge an old man enjoying
himself."

The Walrus looked amazedly at William moving in three directions at once with his face aflame.

"It's all right," said William. "He's giving
us cooking-lessons." Then—the words came
into his mouth by themselves—"I'll take the
responsibility."

"Yes, yes! He knew I could cook. Quite
a young Sherlock he is! *You* carry on." Mr.
Marsh turned his back on the Walrus and despatched William again with some orders to his
shop across the road. "And you'd better tell
'em to put 'em all in a basket," he cried after him.

William returned with a fair assortment of
mixed material, including eggs, two rashers of
bacon, and a packet of patent flour, concerning
which last Mr. Marsh said things no baker should
say about his own goods. The frying-pan came
out of the push-cart, with some other oddments,
and it was not till after it was greased that Mr.
Marsh demanded William's name. He got it in

full, and it produced strange effects on the little
fat man.

" An' 'ow do you spell your middle name?"
he asked.

" G-l-a-double-s-e," said William.

" Might that be your mother's?" William
nodded. " Well! Well! I wonder now! I *do*
wonder. It's a great name. There was a Sawyer
in the cooking line once, but 'e was a Frenchman
and spelt it different. Glasse is serious though.
And you say it was your ma's?" He fell into an
abstraction, frying-pan in hand. Anon, as he
cracked an egg miraculously on its edge—
" Whether you're a descendant or not, it's worth
livin' up to, a name like that."

" Why? " said William, as the egg slid into
the pan and spread as evenly as paint under an
expert's hand.

" I'll tell you some day. She was a very great
cook—but she'd have come expensive at to-day's
prices. Now, you take the pan an' I'll draw me
own conclusions."

The boy worked the pan over the level red fire
with a motion that he had learned somehow or
other while " boiling up " things for his uncle.
It seemed to him natural and easy. Mr. Marsh
watched in unbroken silence for at least two
minutes.

" It's early to say—yet," was his verdict.

" But I 'ave 'opes. You 'ave good 'ands, an' your knowin' I was a cook shows you 'ave the instinck. *If* you 'ave got the Touch—mark you, I only say if —but *if* you 'ave anything like the Genuine Touch, you're provided for for life. *An'* further—don't tilt her that way!—you 'old your neighbours, friends and employers in the 'ollow of your 'and."

" How do you mean? " said William, intent on his egg.

" Everything which a man *is* depends on what 'e puts inside 'im," was the reply. " A good cook's a King of men—besides being thunderin' well off if 'e don't drink. It's the only sure business in the whole round world; and *I*'ve been round it eight times, in the Mercantile Marine, before I married the second Mrs. M."

William, more interested in the pan than Mr. Marsh's marriages, made no reply. " Yes, a good cook," Mr. Marsh went on reminiscently, " even on Board o' Trade allowance, 'as brought many a ship to port that 'ud otherwise 'ave mut'nied on the 'igh seas."

The eggs and bacon mellowed together. Mr. Marsh supplied some wonderful last touches and the result was eaten, with the Walrus's help, sizzling out of the pan and washed down with some stone ginger-beer from the convenient establishment of Mr. E. M. Marsh outside the Park wall.

" I've ruined me dinner," Mr. Marsh confided to the boys, " but I 'aven't enjoyed myself like this, not since Noah was an able seaman. You wash up, young Sherlock, an' I'll tell you something."

He filled an ancient pipe with eloquent tobacco, and while William scoured the pan, he held forth on the art and science and mystery of cooking as inspiredly as Mr. Jorrocks, Master of Foxhounds, had lectured upon the Chase. The burden of his song was Power—power which, striking directly at the stomach of man, makes the rudest polite, not to say sycophantic, towards a good cook, whether at sea, in camp, in the face of war, or (here he embellished his text with personal experiences) the crowded competitive cities where a good meal was as rare, he declared, as silk pyjamas in a pig-sty. " An' mark you," he concluded, " three times a day the 'aughtiest and most overbearin' of 'em all 'ave to come crawling to you for a round belly-full. Put *that* in your pipe and smoke it out, young Sherlock!"

He unloosed his sacrificial apron and rolled away.

The Boy Scout is used to strangers who give him good advice on the smallest provocation; but strangers who fill you up with bacon and eggs and ginger-beer are few.

" What started it all?" the Walrus demanded.

" Well, I can't exactly say," William answered,

and as he had never been known to give a coherent account of anything, the Walrus returned to his wires, and William lay out and dreamed in the fern among the cattle-flies. He had dismissed The Prawn altogether from his miraculously enlarging mind. Very soon he was on the High Seas, a locality which till that instant had never appealed to him, in a gale, issuing bacon and eggs to crews on the edge of mutiny. Next, he was at war, turning the tides of it to victory for his own land by meals of bacon and eggs that brought bemedalled Generals in troops like Pelicans, to his fireplace. Then he was sustaining his uncle, at the door of an enormous restaurant, with plates of bacon and eggs sent out by gilded commission-aires such as guard the cinemas, while his uncle wept with gratitude and remorse, and The Prawn, badges and all, begged for scraps.

His chin struck his chest and half waked him to fresh flights of glory. He might have the Genuine Touch, Mr. Marsh had said it. Moreover, he, the Mug, had a middle name which filled that great man with respect. All the 47th Postal District should ring with that name, even to the exclusion of the racing-news, in its evening papers. And on his return from camp, or perhaps a day or two later, he would defy his very uncle and escape for ever from the foul business of French-polishing.

Here he slept generously and dreamlessly till evening, when the Pelicans returned, their pouches full of samples of uncookable vegetables and insects, and the Walrus made his report of the day's Camp doings to the Scoutmaster.

" Wait a minute, Walrus. You say the Mug actually *did* the cooking?"

" Mr. Marsh had him under instruction, sir. But the Mug did a lot of it—he held the pan over the fire. I saw him, sir. And he washed up afterwards."

" Did he?" said the Scoutmaster lightly. " Well, that's something." But when the Walrus had gone Mr. Hale smote thrice upon his bare knees and laughed, as a Scout should, without noise.

He thanked Mr. Marsh next morning for the interest he had shown in the camp, and suggested (this was while he was buying many very solid buns for a route-march) that nothing would delight the Pelicans more than a few words from Mr. Marsh on the subject of cookery, if he could see his way to it.

" Quite so," said Mr. Marsh. " *I*'m worth listenin' to. Well! Well! I'll be along this evening, and, maybe, I'll bring some odds and ends with me. Send over young Sherlock-Glasse to 'elp me fetch 'em. *That*'s a boy with 'is stummick in the proper place. 'Know anything about 'im?"

Mr. Hale knew a good deal, but he did not

tell it all. He suggested that William himself should be approached, and would excuse him from the route-march for that purpose.

"Route-march!" said Mr. Marsh in horror. "Lor! The very worst use you can make of your feet is walkin' on 'em. 'Gives you bunions. Besides, 'e ain't got the figure for marches. 'E's a cook by build as well as instinck. 'Eavy in the run, oily in the skin, broad in the beam, short in the arm, *but*, mark you, light on the feet. That's the way cooks ought to be issued. You never 'eard of a really good *thin* cook yet, did you? No. Nor me. An' I've known millions that called 'emselves cooks."

Mr. Hare regretted that he had not studied the natural history of cooks, and sent William over early in the day.

Mr. Marsh spoke to the Pelicans for an hour that evening beside an open wood fire, from the ashes of which he drew forth (talking all the while) wonderful hot cakes called "dampers"; while from its top he drew off pans full of "lobscouse," which he said was not to be confounded with "salmagundi," and a hair-raising compound of bacon, cheese and onions all melted together. And while the Pelicans ate, he convulsed them with mirth or held them breathless with anecdotes of the High Seas and the World, so that the vote of thanks they passed him at the end waked all the

cows in the Park. But William sat wrapped in
visions, his hands twitching sympathetically to
Mr. Marsh's wizardry among the pots and pans.
He knew now what the name of Glasse signified;
for he had spent an hour at the back of the baker's
shop reading, in a brown-leather book dated
1767 A.D. and called *The Art of Cookery Made
Plain and Easy by a Lady*, and that lady's name,
as it appeared in facsimile at the head of Chap. I.,
was " H. Glasse." Torture would not have
persuaded him (or Mr. Marsh), by that time, that
she was not his direct ancestress; but, as a matter
of form, he intended to ask his uncle.

When The Prawn, very grateful that Mr.
Marsh had made no reference to his notions of
cookery, asked William what he thought of the
lecture and exhibition, William came out of his
dreams with a start, and " Oh, all right, I suppose,
but I wasn't listening much." Then The Prawn,
who always improved an occasion, lectured him
on lack of attention; and William missed all that
too. The question in his mind was whether his
uncle would let him stay with Mr. Marsh for a
couple of days after Camp broke up, or whether
he would use the reply-paid telegram, which Mr.
Marsh had sent him, for his own French-polishing concerns. When The Prawn's voice ceased,
he not only promised to do better next time, but
added, out of a vast and inexplicable pity that

H

suddenly rose up inside him, " And I'm grateful to you, Prawn.   I am reelly."

On his return to town from that wonder-revealing visit, he found the Pelicans treating him with a new respect.   For one thing, the Walrus had talked about the bacon and eggs; for another, The Prawn, who when he let himself go could be really funny, had given some artistic imitations of Mr. Marsh's comments on his cookery. Lastly, Mr. Hale had laid down that William's future employ would be to cook for the Pelicans when they camped abroad.   " And look out that you don't poison us too much," he added.

There were occasional mistakes and some very flat failures, but the Pelicans swallowed them all loyally; no one had even a stomach-ache, and the office of Cook's mate to William was in great demand.   The Prawn himself sought it next Spring when the Troop stole a couple of fair May days on the outskirts of a brick-field, and were very happy.   But William set him aside in favour of a new and specially hopeless recruit; oily-skinned, fat, short-armed, but light on his feet, and with some notion of lifting pot-lids without wrecking or flooding the whole fireplace.

" You see, Prawn," he explained, " cookin' isn't a thing one can just pick up."

" Yes, I could—watchin' you," The Prawn insisted.

" No.   Mr. Marsh says it's a Gift—same as a Talent."

" D'you mean to tell me Rickworth's got it, then?"

" Dunno.   It's *my* job to find that out— Mr. Marsh says.   Anyway, Rickworth told me he liked cleaning out a fryin' pan because it made him think of what it might be cookin' next time."

" Well, if that isn't silliness, it's just greediness," said The Prawn.   " What about those dampers you were talking of when I bought the fire-lighters for you this morning?"

William drew one out of the ashes, tapped it lightly with his small hazel-wand of office, and slid it over, puffed and perfect, towards The Prawn.

Once again the wave of pity—the Master's pity for the mere consuming Public—swept over him as he watched The Prawn wolf it down.

" I'm grateful to you.   I reely *am*, Prawn," said William Glasse Sawyer.

After all, as he was used to say in later years, if it hadn't been for The Prawn, where would he have been?

PROLOGUE TO THE MASTER-COOK'S TALE

This is what might be called a parody or imitation of the verses of Geoffrey Chaucer, one of the earliest and the greatest of our English poets. It looks difficult to read, but you will find it comes quite easily if you say it aloud, remembering that where there is an accent over the end of a word, that word is pronounced as two syllables—not one. " Snailés," for instance, would be spoken as " snai-les," and so on.

WITH us there rade a Maister-Cook that came
From the Rochelle which is neere Angoulême.
Littel hee was, but rounder than a topp,
And his small berd hadde dipped in manie a soppe.
His honde was smoother than beseemeth mann's,
And his discoorse was all of marzipans,[1]
Of tripes of Caen, or Burdeux snailés swote,[2]
And Seinte Menhoulde wher cooken piggés-foote.[3]
To Thoulouse and to Bress and Carcasson
For pyes and fowles and chesnottes hadde hee wonne; [4]
Of hammés of Thuringie [5] colde hee prate,

[1] A kind of sticky sweetmeat.
[2] Bordeaux snails are specially large and sweet.
[3] They grill pigs'-feet still at St. Menehoulde, not far from Verdun, better than anywhere else in all the world.
[4] Gone—to get pâtés of ducks' liver at Toulouse; fatted poultry at Bourg in Bresse, on the road to Geneva; and very large chestnuts in sugar at Carcassonne, about forty miles from Toulouse.
[5] This would probably be some sort of wild-boar ham from Germany.

And well hee knew what Princes hadde on plate
At Christmas-tide, from Artois to Gascogne.

Lordinges, quod hee, manne liveth nat alone
By bred, but meatés rost and seethed, and broth,
And purchasable [1] deinties, on mine othe.
Honey and hote gingere well liketh hee,
And whalés-flesch mortred [2] with spicerie.
For, lat be all how man denie or carpe,[3]
Him thries a daie his honger maketh sharpe,
And setteth him at boorde [4] with hawkés eyne,
Snuffing what dish is set beforne to deyne,
Nor, till with meate he all-to fill to brim,
None other matter nowher mooveth him.
Lat holie Seintés sterve [5] as bookés boast,
Most mannés soule is in his bellie most.
For, as man thinketh in his hearte is hee,
But, as hee eateth so his thought shall bee.
And Holie Fader's self [6] (with reveraunce)
Oweth to Cooke his port and his presaunce.
Wherbye it cometh past disputison [7]
Cookes over alle men have dominion,
Which follow them as schippe her gouvernail.[8]
Enoff of wordes—beginneth heere my tale :—

[1] Expensive.   [2] Beaten up.   [3] Sneer or despise.
[4] Brings him to table.   [5] Starve.
[6] The Pope himself, who depends on his cook for being healthy and well-fed.
[7] Dispute or argument.
[8] Men are influenced by their cooks as ships are steered by their rudders.

A FLIGHT OF FACT

A FLIGHT OF FACT

Most of this tale actually happened during the War about the years 1916 *or* 1917; *but it was much funnier as I heard it told by a Naval officer than it stands as I have written it from memory. It shows, what one always believed was true—that there is nothing that cannot happen in the Navy.*

H.M.S. *Gardenia* (we will take her name from the Herbaceous Border which belonged to the sloops, though she was a destroyer by profession) came quietly back to her berth some time after midnight, and disturbed half-a-dozen of her sisters as she settled down. They all talked about it next morning, especially *Phlox* and *Stephanotis*, her left- and right-hand neighbours in the big basin on the east coast of England, that was crowded with destroyers.

But the soul of the *Gardenia*—Lieutenant-in-Command H. R. Duckett—was lifted far above insults. What he had done during his last trip had been well done. Vastly more important—*Gardenia* was in for a boiler-clean, which meant four days' leave for her commanding officer.

" Where did you get that fender from, you dockyard burglar?" *Stephanotis* clamoured over his rail, for *Gardenia* was wearing a large coir-matting fender, evidently fresh from store, over her rail. It creaked with newness. " You common thief of the beach, where did you find that new fender?"

The only craft that a destroyer will, sometimes, not steal equipment from is a destroyer; which accounts for the purity of her morals and the loftiness of her conversation, and her curiosity in respect to stolen fillings.

Duckett, unmoved, went below, to return with a valise which he carried on to His Majesty's quarter-deck, and, atop of a suit of rat-catcher clothes, crammed into it a pair of ancient pigskin gaiters.

Here *Phlox*, assisted by her Dandy Dinmont, Dinah, who had been trained to howl at certain notes in her master's voice, gave a spirited and imaginary account of *Gardenia's* return the night before, which was compared to that of an ambulance with a lady-driver. Duckett retaliated by slipping on to his head for one coquettish instant a gravy-coloured soft cloth cap. It was the last straw. *Phlox* and *Stephantois*, who had no hope of any leave for the present, pronounced it an offence, only to be wiped out by drinks.

" All things considered," said Duckett, " I don't care if I *do*. Come along!" and, the hour being what it was, he gave the necessary orders through the wardroom's tiny skylight. The captains came. *Phlox*—Lieutenant-Commander Jerry Marlett, a large and weather-beaten person, docked himself in the arm-chair by the ward-room stove with his cherished Dinah in his arms. Great possessions and much land, inherited from an uncle, had removed him from the Navy on the eve of war. Three days after the declaration of it he was back again, and had been very busy ever since. *Stephanotis*—Lieutenant-in-Command Augustus Holwell Rayne, *alias* " The Damper," because of his pessimism, spread himself out on the settee. He was small and agile, but of gloomy outlook, which a D.S.O. earned, he said, quite by mistake could not lighten. " Horse " Duckett, *Gardenia's* skipper, was a reversion to the primitive Marryat type—a predatory, astute, resourceful pirate, too well known to all His Majesty's dock-yards, a man of easily injured innocence who could always prove an alibi, and in whose ship, if his torpedo-coxswain had ever allowed any one to look there, several sorts of missing Government property might have been found. His ambition was to raise pigs (animals he only knew as bacon) in Shropshire (a county he had never seen) after the war, so he waged his war with zeal to bring that happy day nearer. He sat in the arm-chair by the door, whence he controlled the operations of " Crippen," the wardroom steward, late of

Bolitho's Travelling Circus and Swings, who had taken to the high seas to avoid the attentions of the Police ashore.

As usual, Duckett's character had been blackened by My Lords of the Admiralty, and he was in the midst of a hot campaign against them. An able-seaman's widowed mother had sent a ham to her son, whose name was E. R. Davids. Unfortunately, Engineroom-Artificer E. Davies, who swore that he had both a mother and expectations of hams from her, came across the ham first, and, misreading its address, had had it boiled for, and at once eaten by, the Engineers' mess. E. R. Davids, a vindictive soul, wrote to his mother, who, it seems, wrote to the Admiralty, who, according to Duckett, wrote to him daily every day for a month to know what had become of E. R. Davids' ham. In the meantime the guilty Engineroom-Artificer E. Davies had been transferred to a sloop off the Irish coast.

" An' what the dooce *am* I to do?" Duckett asked his guests plaintively.

" Apply for leave to go to Ireland with a stomach-pump and heave the ham out of Davies," Jerry suggested promptly.

" That's rather a wheeze," said Duckett. " I *had* thought of marrying Davids' mother to settle the case. Anyhow, it was all Crippen's fault for not steering the ham into the wardroom when it came aboard. Don't let it occur again, Crippen. Hams are going to be very scarce."

" Well, now you've got all that off your chest " —Jerry Marlett lowered his voice—" suppose you tell us about what happened—the night before last."

The talk became professional. Duckett produced certain evidence—still damp—in support of the claims that he had sent in concerning the fate of a German submarine, and gave a chain of facts and figures and bearings that the others duly noted.

" And how did your Acting Sub do?" asked Jerry at last.

" Oh, very fair, but I didn't tell him so, of course. They're hard enough to hold at the best of times, these makee-do officers. Have you noticed that they are always above their job— always thinkin' round the corner when they're thinkin' at all? On our way back, this young merchant o' mine—when I'd almost made up my mind to tell him he wasn't as big tripes as he looked—told me his one dream in life was to fly. Fly! He flew alright by the time I'd done with him, but—imagine one's Sub *tellin'* one a thing like that! ' It must be *so* interestin' to fly,' he said. The whole North Sea one blooming burgoo of what-come-nexts, an' this pup complainin' of lack of interest in it! Fly! Fly! When *I* was a Sub-Lootenant——"

He turned pathetically towards The Damper, who had known him in that rank in the Mediterranean.

" There wasn't much flyin' in our day," said The Damper mournfully. " But I can't remember anything else we didn't do."

" Quite so; but we had some decency knocked into us. The new breed wouldn't know decency if they met it on a dungfork. *That's* what I mean."

" When *I* was Actin' Sub," Jerry opened thoughtfully, " in the *Polycarp*—the pious *Polycarp*—Nineteen-O-Seven, I got nine cuts of the best from the Senior Sub for occupyin' the bathroom ten seconds too long. Twenty minutes later, just when the welts were beginnin' to come up, y' know, I was sent off in the gig with a Corporal o' Marines an' a private to fetch the Headman of All the Pelungas aboard. He was wanted for slavery, or barratry, or bigamy or something."

" All the Pelungas?" Duckett repeated with interest. " 'Odd you should mention that part of the world. What are the Pelungas like?"

" Very nice. Hundreds of islands and millions of coral reefs with atolls an' lagoons an' palm-trees, an' all the population scullin' round in outrigger canoes between 'em like a permanent regatta. Filthy navigation, though. *Polycarp*

had to lie five miles out on account of the reefs
(even then our navigator was tearin' his hair), an'
I had an hour's steerin' on hot, hard thwarts.
Talk o' tortures! *You* know. We landed in a
white lather at the boat-steps of the Headman's
island. The Headman wasn't takin' any at first.
He'd drawn up his whole army—three hundred
strong, with old Martini rifles an' a couple of
ancestral seven-pounders—in front of his fort. *We*
didn't know anything about his domestic arrange-
ments. We just dropped in among 'em, so to
say. Then my Corporal of Marines—the fattest
man in the Service bar one—fell down the landin'
steps. The Headman had a Prime Minister—
about as fat as my Corporal—and he helped him
up. Well, *that* broke the ice a bit. The Prime
Minister was a statesman. He poured oil on
the crisis, while the Headman cursed me and the
Navy and the British Government, and I kept
wrigglin' in my white ducks to keep 'em from
drawin' tight on me. *You* know how it feels!
I remember I told the Headman the *Polycarp* 'ud
blow him an' his island out of the water if he
didn't come along quick. She could have done
it—in a week or two; but we were scrubbin'
hammocks at the time. I forgot that little fact
for the minute. I was a bit hot—all over. The
Prime Minister soothed us down again, an' by
and by the Headman said he'd pay us a state call

—as a favour. I didn't care what he called it s'long as he came. So I lay about a quarter of a mile off-shore in the gig, in case the seven-pounders pooped off—I knew the Martinis couldn't hit us at that range—and I waited for him till he shoved off in his State barge—forty rowers a side. Would you believe it, he wanted to take precedence of the White Ensign on the way to the ship? I had to fall him in behind the gig and bring him alongside properly. I was so sore I could hardly get aboard at the finish."

" What happened to the Headman? " said The Damper.

" Nothing. He was acquitted or condemned —I forget which—but he was a perfect gentleman. We used to go sailing with him and his people—dancing with 'em on the beach and all that sort of thing. *I* don't want to meet a nicer community than the Pelungaloos. They aren't used to white men—but they're first-class learners."

" Yes, they *do* seem a cheery crowd," Duckett commented.

" Where have *you* come across them?" said Jerry.

" Nowhere; but this Acting Sub of mine has got a cousin who's been flying down there."

" Flying in All the Pelungas? " Jerry cried. " That's impossible!"

" In these days? Where's your bright lexicon

of youth? Nothing's impossible anywhere now," Duckett replied. " All the best people fly."

" Count me out," Jerry grunted. " We went up once, Dinah, little dog, and it made us both very sick, didn't it? When did it all happen, Horse?"

" Some time last year. This chap, my Sub's cousin—a man called Baxter—went adrift among All the Pelungas in his machine and failed to connect with his ship. He was reported missing for months. Then he turned up again. That's all."

" He was called Baxter?" said The Damper. " Hold on a shake! I wonder if he's ' Beloo ' Baxter, by any chance. There was a chap of that name about five years ago on the China Station. He had himself tattooed all over, regardless, in Rangoon. Then he got as good as engaged to a woman in Hongkong—rich woman too. But the Pusser of his ship gave him away. He had a regular cinema of frogs and dragonflies up his legs. And that was only the beginnin' of the show. So she broke off the engagement, and he half-killed the Pusser, and then he became a Buddhist, or something."

" That couldn't have been this Baxter, or my Sub would have told me," said Duckett. " My Sub's a morbid-minded young animal."

" *Maskee* [1] your Sub's mind!" said Jerry.

[1] Never mind.

I

" What was this Baxter man—plain *or* coloured
—doin' in All *my* Pelungas?"

" As far as I can make out," said Duckett,
" Lootenant Baxter was flyin' in those parts—
with an observer—out of a ship."

" Yes, but what *for?*" Jerry insisted.   " And
what ship?"

" He was flyin' for exercise, I suppose, an' his
ship was the *Cormorang*.   D'you feel wiser?   An'
he flew, an' he flew, an' he flew till, between him
an' his observer and the low visibility and Provi-
dence and all that sort of thing, he lost his ship—
just like some other people I know.   Then he
flapped about huntin' for her till dusk among the
Pelungas, an' then he effected a landin' on the
water."

" A nasty wet business—landin' that way,
Dinah. *We* know," said Jerry into the keen
little cocked ear in his lap.

" Then he taxied about in the dark till he
taxied on to a coral-reef and couldn't get the
machine off.   Coral ain't like mud, is it?"   The
question was to Jerry, but the insult was addressed
to The Damper, who had lately spent eighteen
hours on a soft and tenacious shoal off the East
Coast.   The Damper launched a kick at his host
from where he lay along the settee.

" Then," Duckett went on, " this Baxter-
man got busy with his wireless and S O S'ed like

winkie till the tide came and floated the old bus off the reef, and they taxied over to another island in the dark."

" Thousands of Islands in All the Pelungas," Jerry murmured. " Likewise reefs—hairy ones. What about the reefs?"

" Oh, they kept on hittin' reefs in the dark, till it occurred to them to fire their signal lights to see 'em by. So they went blazin' an' stinkin' and taxyin' up and down the reefs till they found a gap in one of 'em and they taxied bung on to an uninhabited island."

" That must have been good for the machine," was Jerry's comment.

" I don't deny it. I'm only tellin' you what my Sub told me. Baxter wrote it all home to his people, and the letters have been passed round the family. Well, then, o' course, it rained. It rained all the rest of the night, up to the afternoon of the next day. (It always does when you're in a hole.) They tried to start their engine in the intervals of climbin' palm-trees for coco-nuts. They'd only a few buscuits and some water with 'em."

" 'Don't like climbin' palm-trees. It scrapes you raw," The Damper moaned.

" An' when they weren't climbin' or crankin' their engine, they tried to get into touch with the natives on the next nearest island. But the natives weren't havin' any. They took to the bush."

" Ah!" said Jerry sympathetically. " That aeroplane was too much for 'em. Otherwise, they're the most cosy, confidential lot *I* ever met. Well, what happened?"

" Baxter sweated away at his engine till she started up again. Then he flew round lookin' for his ship some more till his petrol ran out. Then he landed close to *another* uninhabited island and tried to taxi up to it."

" Why was he so keen on *un*inhabited islands? I wish I'd been there. *I'd* ha' shown him round the town," said Jerry.

" I don't know his reasons, but that was what he wrote home to his people," Duckett went on. " Not havin' any power by that time, his machine blew on to another reef and there they were! No grub, no petrol, and plenty of sharks! So they snugged her down. I don't know how one snugs down an aeroplane," Duckett admitted, " but Baxter took the necessary steps to reduce the sail-area, and cut the spanker-boom out of the tail-tassels or whatever it is they do on an aeroplane when they want her to be quiet. Anyhow, they more or less secured the bus to that reef so they thought she wouldn't fetch adrift; and they tried to coax a canoe over that happened to be passing. Nothin' doin' *there*! 'Canoe made one bunk of it."

" He tickled 'em the wrong way," Jerry sighed.
" There's a song they sing when they're fishing."
He began to hum dolefully.

" I expect Baxter didn't know that tune,"
Duckett interrupted. " He an' his observer
cursed the canoe a good deal, an' then they went
in for swimmin' stunts all among the sharks, until
they fetched up on the *next* island when they came
to it—it took 'em an hour to swim there—but the
minute they landed the natives all left. 'Seems
to me," said Duckett thoughtfully, " Baxter and
his observer must have spread a pretty healthy
panic scullin' about All the Pelungas in their
shirts."

" But why shirts?" said Jerry. " Those waters
are perfectly warm."

" If you come to that, why *not* shirts?" Duckett
retorted. " A shirt's a badge of civilization——"

" *Maskee* your shirts. What happened after
that?" said The Damper.

" They went to sleep. They were tired by
that time—oddly enough. The natives on *that*
island had left everything standing when they
bunked—fires lighted, chickens runnin' about,
and so forth. Baxter slept in one of the huts.
About midnight some of the bold boys stole back
again. Baxter heard 'em talkin' just outside, and
as he didn't want his face trod on, he said 'Salaam.'
That cleared the island for the second time. The

natives jumped three foot into the air and shoved off."

" Good Lord!" said Jerry impatiently. " *I'd* have had 'em eating out of my hand in ten seconds. 'Salaam' isn't the word to use at all. What he ought to have said——"

" Well, anyhow, he didn't," Duckett replied. " He and his observer had their sleep out an' they woke in the mornin' with ragin' appetites and a strong sense of decency. The first thing they annexed was some native loin-cloths off a bush. Baxter wrote all this home to his people, you know. I expect he was well brought up."

" If he was 'Beloo' Baxter no one would notice ——" The Damper began.

" He wasn't. He was just a simple, virtuous Naval Officer—like me. He an' his observer navigated the island in full dress in search of the natives, but they'd gone and taken the canoe with 'em. Baxter was so depressed at their lack of confidence that he killed a chicken an' plucked it and drew it (I bet neither of you know how to draw fowls) an' boiled it and ate it all at once."

" Didn't he feed his observer?" The Damper asked. " I've a little brother what's an observer up in the air. I'd hate to think he——"

" The observer was kept busy wavin' his shirt on the beach in order to attract the attention of local fishin' craft. That was what *he* was for.

After breakfast Baxter joined him an' the two of 'em waved shirts for two hours on the beach. An' that's the sort of thing my Sub prefers to servin' with me!—*Me!* After a bit, the Pelungaloos decided that they must be harmless lunatics, and one canoe stood pretty close in, an' they swam out to her. But here's a curious thing! Baxter wrote his people that, when the canoe came, his observer hadn't any shirt at all. 'Expect he'd expended it wavin' for succour. But Baxter's shirt was all right. He went out of his way to tell his people so. An' my Sub couldn't see the humour of it one little bit. How does it strike you?"

"Perfectly simple," said Jerry. "Lootenant Baxter as executive officer in charge took his subordinate's shirt owin' to the exigencies of the Service. I'd ha' done the same. Pro-ceed."

"There's worse to follow. As soon as they got aboard the canoe and the natives found they didn't bite, they cottoned to 'em no end. 'Gave 'em grub and dry loin-cloths and betel-nut to chew. What's betel-nut like, Jerry?"

"Grateful an' comfortin'. Warms you all through and makes you spit pink. It's non-intoxicating."

"Oh! I've never tried it. Well then, there was Baxter spittin' pink in a loin-cloth an' a canoe-ful of Pelungaloo fishermen, with his shirt dryin' in the breeze. 'Got that? Well, then his aero-plane, which he thought he had secured to the reef of the next island, began to drift out to sea. That boy had to keep his eyes open, I tell you. He wanted the natives to go in and makee-catchee the machine, and there was a big palaver about it. They naturally didn't care to compromise them-selves with strange idols, but after a bit they lined up a dozen canoes—no, eleven, to be precise— Baxter was awfully precise in his letters to his people—an' tailed on to the aeroplane an' towed it to an island."

"Excellent," said Jerry Marlett, the complete Lieutenant-Commander. "I was gettin' worried about His Majesty's property. Baxter must have had a way with him. A loin-cloth ain't uniform, but it's dashed comfortable. An' how did All my Pelungaloos treat 'em?"

"We-ell!" said Duckett, "Baxter was writin' home to his people, so I expect he toned things down a bit, but, readin' between the lines, it looks as if—an' *that's* why my Sub wants to take up flyin', of course!—it looks as if, from then on, they had what you might call Garden-of-Eden picnics for weeks an' weeks. The natives put 'em under a guard o' sorts just for the look of the thing, while the news was sent to the Headman, but as far as I can make out from my Sub's reminiscences of Baxter's letters, their guard consisted of the

entire male and female population goin' in
swimmin' with 'em twice a day. At night they
had concerts—native songs *versus* music-hall—in
alternate what d'you call 'em? Anti-somethings.
'Phone, ain't it?'"

"They *are* a musical race! I'm glad he
struck that side of their nature," Jerry murmured.

"I'm envious," Duckett protested. "Why
should the Flyin' Corps get all the plums? But
Baxter didn't forget His Majesty's aeroplane.
He got 'em to tow it to his island o' delights, and
in the evenings he an' his observer, between the
musical turns, used to give the women electric
shocks off the wireless. And, one time, he told
his observer to show 'em his false teeth, and when
he took 'em out the people all bolted."

"But that's in Rider Haggard. It's in *King
Solomon's Mines*," The Damper remarked.

"P'raps that's what put it into Baxter's head
then," said Duckett. "Or else," he suggested
warily, "Baxter wanted to crab his observer's
chances with some lady."

"Then he was a fool," The Damper snarled.
"It might have worked the other way. It generally does."

"Well, one can't foresee everything," said
Duckett. "Anyhow, Baxter didn't complain.
They lived there for weeks and weeks, singin'
songs together and bathin' an'—oh, yes!—

gamblin'. Baxter made a set of dice too. He doesn't seem to have neglected much. He said it was just to pass the time away, but I wonder what he threw for. I wish I knew him. His letters to his people are too colourless. What a life he must have led! Women, dice and song, an' your pay rollin' up behind you in perfect safety with no exertion on your part."

" There's a dance they dance on moonlight nights," said Jerry, " with just a few banana leaves—— Never mind. Go ahead! "

" All things bright and beautiful—fineesh," Duckett mourned. " Presently the Headman of All the Pelungas came along—— "

" 'My friend? I hope it was. A first-class sportsman," said Jerry.

" Baxter didn't say. Anyhow, he turned up and they were taken over to the capital island till they could be sent back to their own ship. The Headman did 'em up to the nines in every respect while they were with him (Baxter's quite enthusiastic over it, even in writin' to his own people), but, o' course, there's nothing like first love, is there? They must have felt partin' with their first loves. *I* always do. And then they were put into the full uniform of All the Pelungaloo Army. What's that like, Jerry? You've seen it."

" It's a cross between a macaw an' a rainbow-ended mandrill. Very tasty."

" Just as they were gettin' used to that, and they'd taught the Headman and his Court to sing: ' Hello!   Hello!   Who's your lady friend?' they were embarked on a dirty common sailin' craft an' taken over the ocean and returned to the *Cormorang*, which, o' course, had reported 'em missing and dead months before.   They had one final kick-up before returnin' to duty.   You see, they'd both grown torpedo-beards in the Pelungas, and they were both in Pelungaloo uniform.   Consequently, when they went aboard the *Cormorang* they weren't recognized till they were half-way down to their cabins."

" And then? " both Captains asked at once.

" That's where Baxter breaks off—even though he's writin' to his own people.   He's so apologetic to 'em for havin' gone missin' and worried 'em, an' he's so sinful proud of havin' taught the Headman music-hall songs, that he only said that they had ' some reception aboard the *Cormorang*.'   It lasted till midnight."

" It is possible.   What about their machine?" said Jerry.

" The *Cormorang* ran down to the Pelungas and retrieved it all right.   But *I* should have liked to have seen that reception.   There is nothing I'd ha' liked better than to have seen that reception.   And it isn't as if I hadn't seen a reception or two either."

"The leaf-signal is made, sir," said the Quartermaster at the door.

"Twelve-twenty-four train," Duckett muttered. "Can do." He rose, adding, "I'm going to scratch the backs of swine for the next three days. G'wout!"

The well-trained servant was already fleeting along the edge of the basin with his valise. *Stephanotis* and *Phlox* returned to their own ships, loudly expressing envy and hatred. Duckett paused for a moment at his gangway rail to beckon to his torpedo-coxswain, a Mr. Wilkins, a peace-time sailor of mild and mildewed aspect who had followed Duckett's shady fortunes for some years.

"Wilkins," he whispered, "where *did* we get that new starboard fender of ours from?"

"Orf the dredger, sir. She was asleep when we came in," said Wilkins through lips that scarcely seemed to move. "But our port one come orf the water-boat. We 'ad to over'aul our moorin's in the skiff last night, sir, and we—er— found it on 'er."

"Well, well, Wilkins. Keep the home fires burning," and Lieutenant-in-Command H. R. Duckett sped after his servant in the direction of the railway-station. But not so fast that he could outrun a melody played aboard the *Phlox* on a concertina to which manly voices bore the burden:

When the enterprisin' burglar ain't aburglin'—ain't aburglin',
　　When the cut-throat is not occupied with crime—'pied with
　　　crime.
He loves to hear the little brook agurglin'——

Moved, Heaven knows whether by conscience or kindliness, Lieutenant Duckett smiled at the policeman on the Dockyard gates.

"STALKY"

" STALKY "

This happens to be the first story that was written concerning the adventures and performances of three schoolboys—" Stalky," McTurk and " Beetle." For some reason or other, it was never put into the book, called " Stalky & Co.," that was made out of the stories. A certain amount of it, I am sorry to say, is founded on fact, though that is no recommendation; and the only moral that I can see in it is, that when for any reason you happen to get into a tight place, you have a better chance of coming out of it comfortably if you keep your head than if you get excited and don't stop to think.

" AND then," it was a boy's voice, curiously level and even, " De Vitré said we were beastly funks not to help, and *I* said there were too many chaps in it to suit us. Besides, there's bound to be a mess somewhere or other, with old De Vitré in charge. Wasn't I right, Beetle? "

" And, anyhow, it's a silly biznai, bung through. What'll they *do* with the beastly cows when they've got 'em? You can milk a cow—if she'll stand still. That's all right, but drivin' 'em about—— "

" You're a pig, Beetle."

" No, I ain't. What *is* the sense of drivin' a

lot of cows up from the Burrows to—to—where
is it?"

" They're tryin' to drive 'em up to Toowey's
farmyard at the top of the hill—the empty one,
where we smoked last Tuesday. It's a revenge.
Old Vidley chivied De Vitré twice last week for
ridin' his ponies on the Burrows; and De Vitré's
goin' to lift as many of old Vidley's cattle as he
can and plant 'em up the hill. He'll muck it,
though—with Parsons, Orrin and Howlett helpin'
him. They'll only yell, an' shout, an' bunk if they
see Vidley."

" *We* might have managed it," said McTurk
slowly, turning up his coat-collar against the rain
that swept over the Burrows. His hair was of
the dark mahogany red that goes with a certain
temperament.

" We should," Corkran replied with equal
confidence. " But they've gone into it as if it
was a sort of spadger-hunt. I've never done any
cattle-liftin', but it seems to me-e-e that one might
just as well be stalky about a thing as not."

The smoking vapours of the Atlantic drove in
wreaths above the boys' heads. Out of the mist
to windward, beyond the grey bar of the Pebble
Ridge, came the unceasing roar of mile-long
Atlantic rollers. To leeward, a few stray ponies
and cattle, the property of the Northam potwallopers, and the unwilling playthings of the boys

in their leisure hours, showed through the haze.
The three boys had halted by the Cattle-gate
which marks the limit of cultivation, where the
fields come down to the Burrows from Northam
Hill.   Beetle, shock-headed and spectacled, drew
his nose to and fro along the wet top-bar; McTurk
shifted from one foot to the other, watching the
water drain into either print; while Corkran
whistled through his teeth as he leaned against
a sod-bank, peering into the mist.

A grown or sane person might have called the
weather vile; but the boys at that School had not
yet learned the national interest in climate.   It
was a little damp, to be sure; but it was always
damp in the Easter term, and sea-wet, they held,
could not give one a cold under any circumstances.
Mackintoshes were things to go to church in, but
crippling if one had to run at short notice across
heavy country.   So they waited serenely in the
downpour, clad as their mothers would not have
cared to see.

" I say, Corky," said Beetle, wiping his spec-
tacles for the twentieth time, " if we aren't going
to help De Vitré, what are we here for?"

" We're goin' to watch," was the answer.
" Keep your eye on your Uncle and he'll pull you
through."

" It's an awful biznai, driving cattle—in open
country," said McTurk, who, as the son of an

Irish baronet, knew something of these operations.
" They'll have to run half over the Burrows after
'em.   'S'pose they're ridin' Vidley's ponies?"

" De Vitré's sure to be.   He's a dab on a
horse.   Listen!   What a filthy row they're making.   They'll be heard for miles."

The air filled with whoops and shouts, cries,
words of command, the rattle of broken golf-clubs,
and a clatter of hooves.   Three cows with their
calves came up to the Cattle-gate at a milch-
canter, followed by four wild-eyed bullocks and
two rough-coated ponies.   A fat and freckled
youth of fifteen trotted behind them, riding bare-
back and brandishing a hedge-stake.   De Vitré,
up to a certain point, was an inventive youth, with
a passion for horse-exercise that the Northam
farmers did not encourage.   Farmer Vidley, who
could not understand that a grazing pony likes
being galloped about, had once called him a thief,
and the insult rankled.   Hence the raid.

" Come on," he cried over his shoulder.
" Open the gate, Corkran, or they'll all cut back
again.   We've had no end of bother to get 'em.
Oh, won't old Vidley be wild!"

Three boys on foot ran up, " shooing " the
cattle in excited and amateur fashion, till they
headed them into the narrow, high-banked Devonshire lane that ran uphill.

" Come on, Corkran,   It's no end of a lark,"

pleaded De Vitré; but Corkran shook his head. The affair had been presented to him after dinner that day as a completed scheme, in which he might, by favour, play a minor part. And Arthur Lionel Corkran, No. 104, did not care for lieutenancies.

"You'll only be collared," he cried, as he shut the gate. "Parsons and Orrin are no good in a row. You'll be collared sure as a gun, De Vitré."

"Oh, you're a beastly funk!" The speaker was already hidden by the fog.

"Hang it all," said McTurk. "It's about the first time we've ever tried a cattle-lift at the Coll. Let's———"

"Not much," said Corkran firmly; "keep your eye on your Uncle." His word was law in these matters, for experience had taught them that if they manœuvred without Corkran they fell into trouble.

"You're wrathy because you didn't think of it first," said Beetle. Corkran kicked him thrice calmly, neither he nor Beetle changing a muscle the while.

"No, I ain't; but it isn't stalky enough for me."

"Stalky," in their school vocabulary, meant clever, well-considered and wily, as applied to plans of action; and "stalkiness" was the one virtue Corkran toiled after.

" 'Same thing," said McTurk. " You think you're the only stalky chap in the Coll."

Corkran kicked him as he had kicked Beetle; and even as Beetle, McTurk took not the faintest notice. By the etiquette of their friendship, this was no more than a formal notice of dissent from a proposition.

" They haven't thrown out any pickets," Corkran went on (that school prepared boys for the Army). " You ought to do that—even for apples. Toowey's farmyard may be full of farm-chaps."

" 'Twasn't last week," said Beetle, " when we smoked in that cart-shed place. It's a mile from any house, too."

Up went one of Corkran's light eyebrows. " Oh, Beetle, I *am* so tired o' kickin' you! Does that mean it's empty *now*? They ought to have sent a fellow ahead to look. They're simply bound to be collared. An' where'll they bunk to if they have to run for it? Parsons has only been here two terms. *He* don't know the lie of the country. Orrin's a fat ass, an' Howlett bunks from a guv'nor " [vernacular for any native of Devon engaged in agricultural pursuits] " as far as he can see one. De Vitré's the only decent chap in the lot, an'—an' *I* put him up to usin' Toowey's farmyard."

' Well, keep your hair on," said Beetle.

" What are we going to do? It's hefty damp here."

" Let's think a bit." Corkran whistled between his teeth and presently broke into a swift, short double-shuffle. " We'll go straight up the hill and see what happens to 'em. Cut across the fields; an' we'll lie up in the hedge where the lane comes in by the barn—where we found that dead hedgehog last term. Come on!"

He scrambled over the earth bank and dropped on to the rain-soaked plough. It was a steep slope to the brow of the hill where Toowey's barns stood. The boys took no account of stiles or footpaths, crossing field after field diagonally, and where they found a hedge, bursting through it like beagles. The lane lay on their right flank, and they heard much lowing and shouting in that direction.

" Well, if De Vitré isn't collared," said McTurk, kicking off a few pounds of loam against a gate-post, " he jolly well ought to be."

" We'll get collared, too, if you go on with your nose up like that. Duck, you ass, and stalk along under the hedge. We can get quite close up to the barn," said Corkran. " There's no sense in not doin' a thing stalkily while you're about it."

They wriggled into the top of an old hollow double hedge less than thirty yards from the big

black-timbered barn with its square outbuildings.
Their ten-minutes' climb had lifted them a couple
of hundred feet above the Burrows. As the
mists parted here and there, they could see its
great triangle of sodden green, tipped with yellow
sand-dunes and fringed with white foam, laid out
like a blurred map below. The surge along the
Pebble Ridge made a background to the wild
noises in the lane.

" What did I tell you?" said Corkran, peering
through the stems of the quickset which commanded a view of the farmyard. " Three farm-
chaps—getting out dung—with pitchforks. It's
too late to head off De Vitré. We'd be collared
if we showed up. Besides, they've heard 'em.
They couldn't help hearing. What asses!"

The natives, brandishing their weapons, talked
together, using many times the word " Colleger."
As the tumult swelled, they disappeared into
various pens and byres. The first of the cattle
trotted up to the yard-gate, and De Vitré felicitated
his band.

" That's all right," he shouted. " Oh, won't
old Vidley be wild! Open the gate, Orrin, an'
whack 'em through. They're pretty warm."

" So'll you be in a minute," muttered McTurk
as the raiders hurried into the yard behind the
cattle. They heard a shout of triumph, shrill
yells of despair; saw one Devonian guarding the

gate with a pitchfork, while the others, alas! captured all four boys.

"Of all the infernal, idiotic, lower-second asses!" said Corkran. "They haven't even taken off their house-caps." These dainty confections of primary colours were not issued, as some believe, to encourage House-pride or *esprit de corps*, but for purposes of identification from afar, should the wearer break bounds or laws. That is why, in time of war, any one but an idiot wore his inside out.

"Aie! Yeou young rascals. We've got 'e! Whutt be doin' to Muster Vidley's bullocks?"

"Oh, we found 'em," said De Vitré, who bore himself gallantly in defeat. "Would you like 'em?"

"Found 'em! They bullocks drove like that — all heavin' an' penkin' an' hotted! Oh! Shameful. Yeou've nigh to killed the cows—lat alone stealin' 'em. They sends pore boys to jail for half o' this."

"That's a lie," said Beetle to McTurk, turning on the wet grass.

"I know; but they always say it. 'Member when they collared us at the Monkey Farm that Sunday, with the apples in your topper?"

"My Aunt! They're goin' to lock 'em up an' send for Vidley," Corkran whispered, as one of the captors hurried downhill in the direction

of Appledore, and the prisoners were led into
the barn.

" But they haven't taken their names and
numbers, anyhow," said Corkran, who had fallen
into the hands of the enemy more than once.

" But they're bottled! Rather sickly for De
Vitré," said Beetle. " It's one lickin' anyhow,
even if Vidley don't hammer him. The Head's
rather hot about gate-liftin', and poachin', an' all
that sort of thing. He won't care for cattle-
liftin' much."

" It's awfully bad for cows, too, to run 'em
about in milk," said McTurk, lifting one knee
from a sodden primrose-tuft. " What's the next
move, Corky?"

" We'll get into the old cart-shed where we
smoked. It's next to the barn. We can cut
across over while they're inside and climb in
through the window."

" S'pose we're collared?" said Beetle, cram-
ming his house-cap into his pocket. Caps may
tumble off, so one goes into action bare-headed.

" That's just it. They'd never dream of any
more chaps walkin' bung into the trap. Besides,
we can get out through the roof if they spot us.
Keep your eye on your Uncle. Come on," said
Corkran.

A swift dash carried them to a huge clump of
nettles, beneath the unglazed back window of

the cart-shed. Its open front, of course, gave
on to the barnyard.

They scrambled through, dropped among the
carts, and climbed up into the rudely boarded
upper floor that they had discovered a week before
when in search of retirement. It covered a half
of the building and ended in darkness at the barn
wall. The roof-tiles were broken and displaced.
Through the chinks they commanded a clear
view of the barnyard, half filled with disconsolate
cattle, steaming sadly in the rain.

" You see," said Corkran, always careful to
secure his line of retreat, " if they bottle us up
here, we can squeeze out between these rafters,
slide down the roof, an' bunk. They couldn't
even get out through the window. They'd have
to run right round the barn. Now are you
satisfied, you burbler?"

" Huh! You only said that to make quite
sure yourself," Beetle retorted.

" If the boards weren't all loose, I'd kick
you," growled Corkran. " 'No sense gettin' into
a place you can't get out of. Shut up and listen."

A murmur of voices reached them from the
end of the attic. McTurk tiptoed thither with
caution.

" Hi! It leads through into the barn. You
can get through. Come along!" He fingered
the boarded wall.

" What's the other side?" said Corkran the cautious.

" Hay, you idiot." They heard his boot-heels click on wood, and he had gone.

At some time or other sheep must have been folded in the cart-shed, and an inventive farm-hand, sooner than take the hay round, had dis-placed a board in the barn-side to thrust fodder through. It was in no sense a lawful path, but twelve inches in the square is all that any boy needs.

" Look here!" said Beetle, as they waited for McTurk's return. " The cattle are coming in out of the wet."

A brown, hairy back showed some three feet below the half-floor, as one by one the cattle shouldered in for shelter among the carts below, filling the shed with their sweet breath.

" That blocks our way out, unless we get out by the roof, an' that's rather too much of a drop, unless we have to," said Corkran. " They're all bung in front of the window, too. What a day we're havin'!"

" Corkran! Beetle!" McTurk's whisper shook with delight. " You can see 'em; I've seen 'em. They're in a blue funk in the barn, an' the two clods are makin' fun of 'em—horrid. Orrin's tryin' to bribe 'em an' Parsons is nearly blubbin'. Come an' look! I'm in the hayloft.

Get through the hole. Don't make a row,
Beetle."

Lithely they wriggled between the displaced
boards into the hay and crawled to the edge of
the loft. Three years' skirmishing against a hard
and unsympathetic peasantry had taught them
the elements of strategy. For tactics they looked
to Corkran; but even Beetle, notoriously absent-
minded, held a lock of hay before his head as he
crawled. There was no haste, no betraying
giggle, no squeak of excitement. They had
learned, by stripes, the unwisdom of these things.
But the conference by a root-cutter on the barn
floor was deep in its own affairs; De Vitré's party
promising, entreating, and cajoling, while the
natives laughed like Inquisitors.

" Wait till Muster Vidley an' Muster Toowey
—yis, an' the policemen come," was their only
answer. " 'Tis about time to go to milkin'.
What'ull us do?"

" Yeou go milk, Tom, an' I'll stay long o'
the young gentlemen," said the bigger of the
two, who answered to the name of Abraham.
" Muster Toowey, he'm laike to charge yeou for
usin' his yard so free. Iss fai! Yeou'll be
wopped proper. 'Rackon yeou'll be askin' for
junkets to set in this week o' Sundays to come.
But Muster Vidley, he'll give 'ee the best leatherin'
of all. He'm passionful, I tal 'ee."

Tom stumped out to milk. The barn doors closed behind him, and in the fading light a great gloom fell on all but Abraham, who discoursed eloquently on Mr. Vidley, his temper and strong arm.

Corkran turned in the hay and retreated to the attic, followed by his army.

" No good," was his verdict. " I'm afraid it's all up with 'em. We'd better get out."

" Yes, but look at these beastly cows," said McTurk, spitting on to a heifer's back. " It'll take us a week to shove 'em away from the window, and that brute Tom'll hear us. He's just across the yard, milkin'."

" Tweak 'em, then," said Corkran. " Hang it, I'm sorry to have to go, though. If we could get that other beast out of the barn for a minute we might make a rescue. Well, it's no good. Tweakons!"

He drew forth a slim, well-worn home-made catapult—the " tweaker " of those days—slipped a buckshot into its supple chamois leather pouch, and pulled to the full stretch of the elastic. The others followed his example. They only wished to get the cattle out of their way, but seeing the backs so near, they deemed it their duty each to choose his bird and to let fly with all their strength.

They were not prepared in the least for what followed. Three bullocks, trying to wheel amid

six close-pressed companions, not to mention
three calves, several carts, and all the lumber of
a general-utility shed, do not turn end-for-end
without confusion. It was lucky for the boys
that they stood a little back on the floor, because
one horned head, tossed in pain, flung up a loose
board at the edge, and it came down lancewise
on an amazed back. Another victim floundered
bodily across the shafts of a decrepit gig, smashing
these and oversetting the wheels. That was more
than enough for the nerves of the assembly. With
wild bellowings and a good deal of left-and-right
butting, they dashed into the barnyard, tails on
end, and began a fine free fight on the midden.
The last cow out hooked down an old set of
harness; it flapped over one eye and trailed
behind her. When a companion trod on it,
which happened every few seconds, she naturally
fell on her knees; and, being a Burrows cow,
with the interests of her calf at heart, attacked the
first passer-by. Half-awed, but wholly delighted,
the boys watched the outburst. It was in full
flower before they even dreamed of a second shot.
Tom came out from a byre with a pitchfork, to
be chased in again by the harnessed cow. A
bullock floundered on the muck-heap, fell, rose
and bedded himself to the belly, helpless and bel-
lowing. The others took great interest in him.

Corkran, through the roof, scientifically

" tweaked " a frisky heifer on the nose, and it is no exaggeration to say that she danced on her hind legs for half a minute.

" Abram!   Oh, Abram!   They'm bewitched. They'm ragin'.   'Tes the milk fever.   They've been drove mad.   Oh, Abram!   They'll horn the bullocks!   They'll horn *me*!   Abram!"

" Bide till I lock the door," quoth Abraham, faithful to his trust.   They heard him padlock the barn door; saw him come out with yet another pitchfork.   A bullock lowered his head, Abraham ran to the nearest pig-pen, where loud squeakings told that he had disturbed the peace of a large family.

" Beetle," snapped Corkran.   " Go in an' get those asses out.   Quick!   We'll keep the cows happy."

A people sitting in darkness and the shadow of monumental lickings, too depressed to be angry with De Vitré, heard a voice from on high saying, " Come up here!   Come on!   Come up! There's a way out."

They shinned up the loft-stanchions without a word; found a boot-heel which they were bidden to take for guide, and squeezed desperately through a hole in darkness, to be hauled out by Corkran.

" Have you got your caps?   Did you give 'em your names and numbers?"

" Yes. No."

" That's all right. Drop down here. Don't stop to jaw. Over the cart—through that window, and bunk! Get *out!*"

De Vitré needed no more. They heard him squeak as he dropped among the nettles, and through the roof-chinks they watched four slight figures disappear into the rain. Tom and Abraham, from byre and pig-pen, exhorted the cattle to keep quiet.

" By gum!" said Beetle; " that *was* stalky. How did you think of it?"

" It was the only thing to do. Anybody could have seen that."

" Hadn't we better bunk, too, now?" said McTurk uneasily.

" Why? *We*'re all right. *We* haven't done anything. I want to hear what old Vidley will say. Stop tweakin', Turkey. Let 'em cool off. Golly! how that heifer danced! I swear I didn't know cows could be so lively. We're only just in time."

" My Hat! Here's Vidley—and Toowey," said Beetle, as the two farmers strode into the yard.

" Gloats! oh, gloats! Fids! oh, fids! Hefty fids and gloats to us!" said Corkran.

These words, in their vocabulary, expressed the supreme of delight. " Gloats " implied

L

more or less of personal triumph, " fids " was
felicity in the abstract, and the boys were tasting
both that day.   Last joy of all, they had had the
pleasure of Mr. Vidley's acquaintance, albeit he
did not love them.   Toowey was more of a
stranger ; his orchards lying over-near to the
public road.

Tom and Abraham together told a tale of
stolen cattle maddened by overdriving; of cows
sure to die in calving, and of milk that would
never return; that made Mr. Vidley swear for
three consecutive minutes in the speech of north
Devon.

" 'Tes tu bad.   'Tes tu bad," said Toowey,
consolingly; " let's 'ope they 'aven't took no
great 'arm.   They be wonderful wild, though."

" 'Tes all well for yeou, Toowey, that sells
them dom Collegers seventy quart a week."

" Eighty," Toowey replied, with the meek
triumph of one who has underbidden his neighbour on public tender; " but that's no odds to
me.   Yeou'm free to leather 'em saame as if
they was yeour own sons.   On my barn-floor
shall 'ee leather 'em."

" Generous old swine!" said Beetle.   " De
Vitré ought to have stayed for this."

" They'm all safe an' to rights," said the
officious Abraham, producing the key.   " Rackon
us'll come in an' hold 'em for yeou.   Hey!   The

cows are fair ragin' still. Us'll have to run for it."

The barn being next to the shed, the boys could not see that stately entry. But they heard.

"Gone an' hided in the hay. Aie! They'm proper afraid," cried Abraham.

"Rout un out! Rout un out!" roared Vidley, rattling a stick impatiently on the root-cutter.

"Oh, my Aunt!" said Corkran, standing on one foot.

"Shut the door. Shut the door, I tal 'ee. Rackon us can find un in the dark. Us don't want un boltin' like rabbits under our elbows." The big barn door closed with a clang.

"My Gum!" said Corkran, which was always his War oath in time of action. He dropped down and was gone for perhaps twenty seconds.

"And *that's* all right," he said, returning at a gentle saunter.

"Hwatt?" McTurk almost shrieked, for Corkran, in the shed below, waved a large key.

"Stalks! Frabjous Stalks! Bottled 'em! all four!" was the reply, and Beetle fell on his bosom. "Yiss. They'm so's to say, like, locked up. If you're goin' to laugh, Beetle, I shall have to kick you again."

"But I must!" Beetle was blackening with suppressed mirth.

"You won't do it here, then." He thrust

the already limp Beetle through the cart-shed
window.   It sobered him; one cannot laugh on
a bed of nettles.   Then Corkran stepped on his
prostrate carcass, and McTurk followed, just as
Beetle would have risen; so he was upset, and the
nettles painted on his cheek a likeness of hideous
eruptions.

"'Thought that 'ud cure you," said Corkran,
with a sniff.

Beetle rubbed his face desperately with dock-
leaves, and said nothing.   All desire to laugh had
gone from him.   They entered the lane.

Then a clamour broke from the barn—a compound noise of horse-like kicks, shaking of door-
panels, and various yells.

"They've found it out," said Corkran. "How
strange!"   He sniffed again.

"Let 'em," said Beetle.   "No one can hear
'em.   Come on up to Coll."

"What a brute you are, Beetle!   You only
think of your beastly self.   Those cows want
milkin'.   Poor dears!   Hear 'em low," said
McTurk.

"Go back and milk 'em yourself, then."
Beetle danced with pain.   "We shall miss Call-
over, hangin' about like this; an' I've got two
black marks this week already."

"Then you'll have fatigue-drill on Monday,"
said Corkran.   "'Come to think of it, I've got

two black marks *aussi*. Hm! This is serious.
This is hefty serious."

" I told you," said Beetle, with vindictive
triumph. " An' we want to go out after that
hawk's nest on Monday. We shall be swottin'
dum-bells, though. *All* your fault. If we'd
bunked with De Vitré at first——"

Corkran paused between the hedgerows.
" Hold on a shake an' don't burble. Keep your
eye on Uncle. Do you know, *I* believe some
one's shut up in that barn. I think we ought to
go and see."

" Don't be a giddy idiot. Come on up to
Coll." But Corkran took no notice of Beetle.

He retraced his steps to the head of the lane,
and, lifting up his voice, cried as in bewilderment,
" Hullo? Who's there? What's that row about?
Who are you?"

" Oh, Peter!" said Beetle, skipping, and forgetting his anguish in this new development.

" Hoi! Hoi! 'Ere! Let us out!" The
answers came muffled and hollow from the black
bulk of the barn, with renewed thunders on the
door.

" Now play up," said Corkran. " Turkey,
you keep the cows busy. 'Member that we've
just discovered 'em. *We* don't know anything.
Be polite, Beetle."

They picked their way over the muck and held

speech through a crack by the door-hinge.   Three
more genuinely surprised boys the steady rain
never fell upon.   And they were so difficult to
enlighten.   They had to be told again and again
by the captives within.

"We've been 'ere for hours an' hours."   That
was Toowey.   "An' the cows to milk, an' all."
That was Vidley.   "The door she blewed against
us an' jammed herself."   That was Abraham.

"Yes, we can see that.   It's jammed on this
side," said Corkran.   "How careless you chaps
are!"

"Oppen un.   Oppen un.   Bash her oppen with
a rock, young gen'elmen!   The cows are milk-
heated an' ragin'.   Haven't you boys no sense?"

Seeing that McTurk from time to time tweaked
the cattle into renewed caperings, it was quite
possible that the boys had some knowledge of a
sort.   But Mr. Vidley was rude.   They told him
so through the door, professing only now to
recognize his voice.

"Humour un if 'e can.   I paid seven-an'-six
for the padlock," said Toowey.   "Niver mind
him.   'Tes only old Vidley."

"Be yeou gwaine to stay a prisoneer an'
captive for the sake of a lock, Toowey?   I'm
shaamed of 'ee.   Rowt un oppen, young gen'elmen!   'Twas a God's own mercy yeou heard us.
Toowey, yeou'm a borned miser."

" It'll be a long job," said Corkran. " Look here. It's near our call-over. If we stay to help you we'll miss it. We've come miles out of our way already—after you."

" Tell yeour master, then, what keeped 'ee— an arrand o' mercy, laike. I'll tal un tu when I bring the milk to-morrow," said Toowey.

" That's no good," said Corkran; " we may be licked twice over by then. You'll have to give us a letter." McTurk, backed against the barn-wall, was firing steadily and accurately into the brown of the herd.

" Yiss, yiss. Come down to my house. My missus shall write 'ee a beauty, young gen'elmen. She makes out the bills. I'll give 'ee just such a letter o' racommendation as I'd give to my own son, if only yeou can humour the lock!"

" Niver mind the lock," Vidley wailed. " Let me get to me pore cows, 'fore they'm dead."

They went to work with ostentatious rattlings and wrenchings, and a good deal of the by-play that Corkran always loved. At last—the noise of unlocking was covered by some fancy hammer-ing with a young boulder—the door swung open and the captives marched out.

" Hurry up, Mister Toowey," said Corkran; " we ought to be getting back. Will you give us that note, please?"

" Some of yeou young gentlemen was drivin'

my cattle off the Burrowses," said Vidley. " I
give 'ee fair warnin', I'll tell yeour masters. I
know *yeou!*" He glared at Corkran with malig-
nant recognition.

McTurk looked him over from head to foot.
" Oh, it's only old Vidley. Drunk again, I
suppose. Well, we can't help that. Come on,
Mister Toowey. We'll go to your house."

" Drunk, am I? I'll drunk 'ee! How do I
know yeou bain't the same lot? Abram, did 'ee
take their names an' numbers?"

" What *is* he ravin' about?" said Beetle.
" Can't you see that if we'd taken your beastly
cattle we shouldn't be hanging round your beastly
barn. 'Pon my Sam, you Burrows guv'nors
haven't any sense———"

" Let alone gratitude," said Corkran. " I
suppose he *was* drunk, Mister Toowey; an' you
locked him in the barn to get sober. Shockin'!
Oh, shockin'!"

Vidley denied the charge in language that the
boys' mothers would have wept to hear.

" Well, go and look after your cows, then,"
said McTurk. " Don't stand there cursin' us
because we've been kind enough to help you out
of a scrape. Why on earth weren't your cows
milked before? *You*'re no farmer. It's long
past milkin'. No wonder they're half crazy.
'Disreputable old bog-trotter, you are. Brush

your hair, sir. . . . I *beg* your pardon, Mister Toowey. 'Hope we're not keeping you."

They left Vidley dancing on the muck-heap, amid the cows, and devoted themselves to propitiating Mr. Toowey on their way to his house. Exercise had made them hungry; hunger is the mother of good manners; and they won golden opinions from Mrs. Toowey.

*　　*　　*　　*　　*

" Three-quarters of an hour late for Call-over, and fifteen minutes late for Lock-up," said Foxy, the school Sergeant, crisply. He was waiting for them at the head of the corridor. " Report to your housemaster, please—an' a nice mess you're in, young gentlemen."

" Quite right, Foxy. Strict attention to dooty does it," said Corkran. " Now where, if we asked you, would you say that his honour Mister Prout might, at this moment of time, be found prouting—eh?"

" In 'is study—as usual, Mister Corkran. He took Call-over."

" Hurrah! Luck's with us all the way. Don't blub, Foxy. I'm afraid you don't catch us this time."

*　　*　　*　　*　　*

" We went up to change, sir, before comin' to you. That made us a little late, sir. We weren't really very late. We were detained—by a———"

" An errand of mercy," said Beetle, and they laid Mrs. Toowey's laboriously written note before him. " We thought you'd prefer a letter, sir. Toowey got himself locked into a barn, and we heard him shouting—it's Toowey who brings the Coll. milk, sir—and we went to let him out."

" There were ever so many cows waiting to be milked," said McTurk; " and of course, he couldn't get at them, sir. They said the door had jammed. There's his note, sir."

Mr. Prout read it over thrice. It was perfectly unimpeachable; but it said nothing of a large tea supplied by Mrs. Toowey.

" Well, I don't like your getting mixed up with farmers and potwallopers. Of course you will not pay any more—er—visits to the Tooweys," said he.

" Of course not, sir. It was really on account of the cows, sir," replied McTurk, glowing with philanthropy.

" And you came straight back?"

" We ran nearly all the way from the Cattle-gate," said Corkran, carefully developing the unessential. " That's one mile, sir. Of course, we had to get the note from Toowey first."

" But it was because we went to change—we were rather wet, sir—that we were *really* late. After we'd reported ourselves to the Sergeant, sir, and he knew we were in Coll., we didn't like to

come to your study all dirty." Sweeter than
honey was the voice of Beetle.

"Very good. Don't let it happen again."
Their housemaster learned to know them better
in later years.

They entered—not to say swaggered—into
Number Nine form-room, where De Vitré, Orrin,
Parsons, and Howlett, before the fire, were still
telling their adventures to admiring associates.
The four rose as one boy.

"What happened to *you*? We just saved
Call-over. Did you stay on? Tell us! Tell
us!"

The three smiled pensively. They were not
distinguished for telling more than was necessary.

"Oh, we stayed on a bit and then we came
away," said McTurk. "That's all."

"You scab! You might tell a chap anyhow."

"'Think so? Well, that's awfully good of you,
De Vitré. 'Pon my sainted Sam, that's awfully
good of you," said Corkran, shouldering into the
centre of the warmth and toasting one slippered
foot before the blaze. "So you really think we
might tell you?"

They stared at the coals and shook with deep,
delicious chuckles.

"My Hat! We *were* stalky," said McTurk.
"I swear we were about as stalky as they make
'em. Weren't we?"

" It was a frabjous Stalk," said Beetle.
" 'Much too good to tell you brutes, though."

The form wriggled under the insult, but made
no motion to avenge it. After all, on De Vitré's
showing, the three had saved the raiders from at
least a public licking.

" It wasn't half bad," said Corkran. " Stalky
is the word."

" *You* were the really stalky one," said
McTurk, one contemptuous shoulder turned to a
listening world. " By Gum! you *were* stalky."

Corkran accepted the compliment and the
name together. " Yes," said he; " keep your eye
on your Uncle Stalky an' he'll pull you through."

" Well, you needn't gloat so," said De Vitré,
viciously; " you look like a stuffed cat."

Corkran, henceforth known as Stalky, took not
the slightest notice, but smiled dreamily.

" My Hat! Yes. Of course," he murmured.
" Your Uncle Stalky—a doocid good name. Your
Uncle Stalky is no end of a stalker. He's a Great
Man. I swear he is. De Vitré, you're an ass—
a putrid ass."

De Vitré would have denied this but for the
assenting murmurs from Parsons and Orrin.

" You needn't rub it in, then."

" But I do. I does. You are such a woppin'
ass. D'you know it? Think over it a bit at prep.
Think it up in bed. Oblige me by thinkin' of it

every half hour till further notice. Gummy!
What an ass you are! But your Uncle Stalky "—
he picked up the form-room poker and beat it
against the mantelpiece—" is a Great Man!"

"Hear, hear," said Beetle and McTurk, who
had fought under that general.

"Isn't your Uncle Stalky a great man, De
Vitré? Speak the truth, you fat-headed old
impostor."

"Yes," said De Vitré, deserted by all his band.
" I—I suppose he is."

" 'Mustn't suppose. *Is* he?"

" Well, he is."

" A Great Man?"

" A Great Man. *Now* won't you tell us?"
said De Vitré pleadingly.

" Not by a heap," said " Stalky " Corkran.

Therefore the tale has stayed untold till to-day.

THE HOUR OF THE ANGEL [1]

Sooner or late—in earnest or in jest—
  (But the stakes are no jest) Ithuriel's Hour
Will spring on us, for the first time, the test
    Of our sole unbacked competence and power
    Up to the limit of our years and dower
Of judgment—or beyond.   But here we have
Prepared long since our garland or our grave.
    For, at that hour, the sum of all our past,
    Act, habit, thought, and passion, shall be cast
    In one addition, be it more or less,
    And as that reading runs so shall we do;
    Meeting, astounded, victory at the last,
    Or, first and last, our own unworthiness.
And none can change us though they die to save!

[1] Ithuriel was that Archangel whose spear had the magic property of showing every one exactly and truthfully what he was.

THE BURNING OF THE
"SARAH SANDS"

THE BURNING OF THE
" SARAH SANDS "

Men have sailed the seas for so many years, and have there done such amazing things in the face of danger, difficulty and death, that no one tale of heroism exists which cannot be equalled by at least scores of others. But since the behaviour of bodies of untried men under trying circumstances is always interesting, and since I have been put in possession of some facts not very generally known, I am trying to tell again the old story of the Sarah Sands, *as an example of long-drawn-out and undefeatable courage and cool-headedness.*

SHE was a small fourmasted, iron-built screw-steamer of eleven hundred tons, chartered to take out troops to India. That was in 1857, the year of the Indian Mutiny, when anything that could sail or steer was in great demand; for troops were being thrown into the country as fast as circumstances allowed—which was not very fast.

Among the regiments sent out was the 54th of the Line, now the Second Battalion of the Dorset Regiment—a good corps, about a hundred years old, with a very fair record of service, but in no special way differing, so far as one could see, from many other regiments. It was despatched

in three ships.   The Headquarters—that is to
say, the Lieutenant-Colonel, the Regimental
books, pay-chest, Band and Colours, which last
represent the very soul of a Battalion—and some
fourteen officers, three hundred and fifty-four rank
and file, and perhaps a dozen women, left Portsmouth on the 15th of August all packed tight in
the *Sarah Sands*.

Her crew, with the exception of the engineers
and firemen, seem to have been foreigners and
pier-head jumpers picked up at the last minute.
They turned out bad, lazy and insubordinate.

The accommodation for the troops was generously described as "inferior," and what men
called "inferior" in 1857 would now be called
unspeakable.   Nor, in spite of the urgent need,
was there any great hurry about the *Sarah Sands*.
She took two long months to reach Capetown, and
she stayed there five days to coal, leaving on the
20th of October.   By this time, the crew were all
but openly mutinous, and the troops, who must
have picked up a little seamanship, had to work
the ship out of harbour.

On the 7th of November, nearly three weeks
later, a squall struck her and carried away her
foremast; and it is to be presumed that the troops
turned to and cleared away the wreckage.   On
the 11th of November the real trouble began, for,
in the afternoon of that day, ninety days out from

Portsmouth, a party of soldiers working in the hold saw smoke coming up from the after-hatch. They were then, maybe, within a thousand miles of the Island of Mauritius, in half a gale and a sea full of sharks.

Captain Castles, the master, promptly lowered and provisioned the boats; got them over-side with some difficulty and put the women into them. Some of the sailors—the engineers, the firemen and a few others behaved well—jumped into the long-boat, lowered it and kept well away from the ship. They knew she carried two magazines full of cartridges, and were taking no chances.

The troops, on the other hand, did not make any fuss, but under their officers' orders cleared out the starboard or right-hand magazine, while volunteers tried to save the Regimental Colours. These stood at the end of the saloon, probably clamped against the partition behind the Captain's chair, and the saloon was full of smoke. Two lieutenants made a dash thither but were nearly suffocated. A ship's quartermaster—Richard Richmond was his name—put a wet cloth over his face, managed to tear down the Colours, and then fainted. A private—and his name was W. Wiles—dragged out both Richmond and the Colours, and the two men dropped senseless on the deck while the troops cheered. That, at least, was a good beginning; for, as I have said, the Colours are the soul of every body of men who fight or work under them.

The saloon must have been one of the narrow, cabin - lined, old - fashioned " cuddies," placed above the screw, and all the fire was in the stern of the ship, behind the engine-room. It was blazing very close to the port or left-hand magazine, and, as an explosion there would have blown the *Sarah Sands* out like a squib, they called for more volunteers, and one of the lieutenants who had been choked in the saloon recovered, went down first and passed up a barrel of ammunition, which was at once hove overboard. After this example, work went on with regularity.

When the men taking out the ammunition fainted, as they did fairly often, they pulled them up with ropes. Those who did not faint, grabbed what explosives they could feel or handle in the smother, and brought them up, and an official and serene quartermaster-sergeant stood on the hatch and jotted down the number of barrels so retrieved in his notebook, as they were thrown into the sea. They pulled out all except two barrels which slid from the arms of a fainting man— there was a fair amount of fainting that evening —and rolled out of reach. Besides these, there were another couple of barrels of signalling powder for the ship's use; but this the troops did not know, and were the more comfortable for their ignorance.

Then the flames broke through the after-deck, the light attracting shoals of sharks, and the mizzen-mast—the farthest aft of all the masts—flared up and went over-side with a crash.   This would have veered the stern of the ship-head to the wind, in which case the flames must have swept forward; but a man with a hatchet—his name is lost—ran along the bulwarks and cut the wreck clear, while the boat full of women surged and rocked at a safe distance, and the sharks tried to upset it with their tails.

A Captain of the 54th—he was a jovial soul, and made jokes throughout the struggle—headed a party of men to cut away the bridge, the deck-cabins, and everything else that was inflammable —this in case of the flames sweeping forward again—while a provident lieutenant, with some more troops, lashed spars and things together for a raft, and other gangs pumped water desperately on to what was left of the saloon and the magazines.

One record says quaintly: " It was necessary to make some deviation from the usual military evolutions while the flames were in progress. The men formed in sections, countermarched round the forward part of the ship, which may perhaps be better understood when it is stated that those with their faces to the after part where the fire raged were on their way to relieve their comrades who had been working below. Those proceeding 'forward' were going to recruit their exhausted strength and prepare for another attack when it came to their turn."

No one seemed to have much hopes of saving the ship so long as the last of the powder was un-accounted for. Indeed, Captain Castles told an officer of the 54th that the game was up, and the officer replied, " We'll fight till we're driven over-board." It seemed he would be taken at his word, for just then the signalling powder and the ammunition-casks went up, and the ship seen from midships aft looked like one floating volcano.

The cartridges spluttered like crackers, and cabin doors and timbers were shot up all over the deck, and two or three men were hurt. But—this is not in any official record—just after the roar of it, when her stern was dipping deadlily, and all believed the *Sarah Sands* was settling for her last lurch, some merry jester of the 54th cried, " Lights out," and the jovial captain shouted back, " All right! We'll keep the old woman afloat yet." Not one man of the troops made any attempt to get on to the rafts; and when they found the ship was still floating they all went back to work double tides.

At this point in the story we come across

Mr. Frazer, the Scotch engineer, who, like most of his countrymen, had been holding his trump-card in reserve. He knew the *Sarah Sands* was built with a water-tight bulkhead behind the engine-room and the coal-bunkers; and he proposed to cut through the bulkhead and pump on the fire. Also, he pointed out that it would be well to remove the coal in the bunkers, as the bulkhead behind was almost red-hot, and the coal was catching light.

So volunteers dropped into the bunkers, each man for the minute or two he could endure it, and shovelled away the singeing, fuming fuel, and other volunteers were lowered into the bonfire aft, and when they could throw no more water on it they were pulled up half roasted.

Mr. Frazer's plan saved the ship, though every particle of wood in the after part of her was destroyed, and a bluish vapour hung over the red-hot iron beams and ties, and the sea for miles about looked like blood under the glare, as they pumped and passed water in buckets, flooding the stern, sluicing the engine-room bulkhead and damping the coal beyond it all through the long night. The very sides of the ship were red-hot, so that they wondered when her plates would buckle and wrench out the rivets and let the whole misery down to the sharks.

The foremast had carried away on the squall

of the 7th of November; the mizzen-mast, as
you know, had gone in the fire; the main-mast,
though wrapped round with wet blankets, was
alight, and everything abaft the main-mast was
one red furnace.   There was the constant danger
of the ship, now broadside on to the heavy seas,
falling off before the heavy wind, and leading the
flames forward again.   So they hailed the boats
to tow and hold her head to wind; but only the
gig obeyed the order.   The others had all they
could do to keep afloat; one of them had been
swamped, though all her people were saved; and
as for the long-boat full of mutinous seamen,
she behaved infamously.   One record says that
" She not only held aloof, but consigned the ship
and all she carried to perdition."   So the *Sarah
Sands* fought for her own life alone, with the
sharks in attendance.

About three on the morning of the 12th of
November, pumping, bucketing, sluicing and
damping, they began to hope that they had bested
the fire.   By nine o'clock they saw steam coming
up from her insides instead of smoke, and at mid-
day they called in the boats and took stock of the
damage.   From the mizzen-mast aft there was
nothing that you could call ship except just the
mere shell of her.   It was all one steaming heap
of scrap-iron with twenty feet of black, greasy
water flooding across the bent and twisted rods,

and in the middle of it all four huge water-tanks rolled to and fro, thundering against the naked sides.

Moreover,—this they could not see till things had cooled down—the powder explosions had blown a hole right through her port quarter, and every time she rolled the sea came in there green. Of the four masts only one was left; and the rudder-head stuck up all bald, black and horrible among the jam of collapsed deck-beams. A photograph of the wreck looks exactly like that of a gutted theatre after the flames and the firemen have done their worst.

They spent the whole of the 12th of November pumping water out as zealously as they had pumped it in. They lashed up the loose, charging tanks as soon as they were cool enough to touch. They plugged the hole at the stern with hammocks, sails, and planks, and a sail over all. Then they rigged up a horizontal bar gripping the rudder-head. Six men sat on planks on one side and six at the other over the empty pit beneath, hauling on to the bar with ropes and letting go as they were told. That made the best steering-gear that they could devise.

On the 13th of November, still pumping, they spread one sail on their solitary mast—it was lucky that the *Sarah Sands* had started with four of them—and took advantage of the trade winds to

make for Mauritius.   Captain Castles, with one
chart and one compass, lived in a tent where some
cabins had once been; and at the end of twelve
more days he sighted land.   Their average run
was about four knots an hour; and, it is no
wonder that as soon as they were off Port Louis,
Mauritius, Mr. Frazer, the Scotch engineer,
wished to start his engines and enter port pro-
fessionally.   The troops looked down into the
black hollow of the ship when the shaft made its
first revolution, shaking the hull horribly; and if
you can realize what it means to be able to see a
naked screw-shaft at work from the upper deck
of a liner, you can realize what had happened to
the *Sarah Sands*.   They waited outside Port
Louis for the daylight, and were nearly dashed to
pieces on a coral reef.   Then the gutted, empty
steamer came in—very dirty, the men's clothes so
charred that they hardly dared to take them off,
and very hungry; but without having lost one
single life.   Port Louis gave them all a public
banquet in the market-place, and the French in-
habitants were fascinatingly polite as only the
French can be.

But the records say nothing of what befell the
sailors who " consigned the ship to perdition."
One account merely hints that " this was no time
for retribution "; but the troops probably ad-
ministered their own justice during the twelve

days' limp to port. The men who were berthed aft, the officers and the women, lost everything they had; and the companies berthed forward lent them clothes and canvas to make some sort of raiment.

On the 20th of December they were all re-embarked on the *Clarendon*. It was poor accommodation for heroes. She had been condemned as a coolie-ship, was full of centipedes and other animals picked up in the Brazil trade; her engines broke down frequently; and her captain died of exposure and anxiety during a hurricane. So it was the 25th of January before she reached the mouth of the Hugli.

By this time—many of the men probably considered this quite as serious as the fire—the troops were out of tobacco, and when they came across the American ship *Hamlet*, Captain Lecran, lying at Kedgeree on the way up the river to Calcutta, the officers rowed over to ask if there was any tobacco for sale. They told the skipper the history of their adventures, and he said: " Well, I'm glad you've come to me, because I have some tobacco. How many are you? " " Three hundred men," said the officers. Thereupon Captain Lecran got out four hundred pounds of best Cavendish as well as one thousand Manilla cigars for the officers, and refused to take payment on the grounds that Americans did not accept anything from shipwrecked people. They were not shipwrecked at the time, but evidently they had been shipwrecked quite enough for Captain Lecran, because when they rowed back a second time and insisted on paying, he only gave them grog, " which," says the record, " caused it to be dark when we returned to our ship." After this " our band played ' Yankee-Doodle,' blue lights were burned, the signal-gun fired "—that must have been a lively evening at Kedgeree— " and everything in our power was had recourse to so as to convey to our American cousins our appreciation of their kindness."

Last of all, the Commander-in-Chief issued a general order to be read at the head of every regiment in the Army. He was pleased to observe that " the behaviour of the 54th Regiment was most praiseworthy, and by its result must render manifest to all the advantage of subordination and strict obedience to orders under the most alarming and dangerous circumstances in which soldiers can be placed."

This seems to be the moral of the tale.

THE LAST LAP

How do we know, by the bank-high river,
  Where the mired and sulky oxen wait,
And it looks as though we might wait for ever,
  How do we know that the floods abate?
There is no change in the current's brawling—
  Louder and harsher the freshet scolds;
Yet we can feel she is falling, falling,
  And the more she threatens the less she holds.
Down to the drift, with no word spoken,
  The wheel-chained wagons slither and slue.
Steady! The back of the worst is broken.
    And—lash your leaders!—we're through—we're
      through!

How do we know, when the port-fog holds us
  Moored and helpless, a mile from the pier,
And the week-long summer smother enfolds us—
  How do we know it is going to clear?
There is no break in the blindfold weather,
  But, one and another, around the bay,
The unseen capstans clink together,
  Getting ready to up and away.
A pennon whimpers—the breeze has found us—
  A headsail jumps through the thinning haze.
The whole hull follows, till—broad around us—
  The clean-swept ocean says: " Go your ways!"

How do we know, when the long fight rages,
   On the old, stale front that we cannot shake,
And it looks as though we were locked for ages,
   How do we know they are going to break?
There is no lull in the level firing,
   Nothing has shifted except the sun.
Yet we can feel they are tiring, tiring,
   Yet we can tell they are ripe to run.
Something wavers, and, while we wonder
   Their centre trenches are emptying out,
And, before their useless flanks go under,
   Our guns have pounded retreat to rout!

THE PARABLE OF BOY JONES

THE PARABLE OF BOY JONES

This tale was written several years before the War, as you can see for yourselves. It is founded on fact, and it is meant to show that one ought to try to recognize facts, even when they are unpleasant and inconvenient.

THE long shed of the Village Rifle Club reeked with the oniony smell of smokeless powder, machine-oil, and creosote from the stop-butt, as man after man laid himself down and fired at the miniature target sixty feet away. The Instructor's voice echoed under the corrugated iron roof.

" Squeeze, Matthews, squeeze! Jerking your shoulder won't help the bullet. . . . Gordon, you're canting your gun to the left. . . . Hold your breath when the sights come on. . . . Fenwick, was that a bull? Then it's only a fluke, for your last at two o'clock was an outer. You don't know where you're shooting."

" I call this monotonous," said Boy Jones, who had been brought by a friend to look at the show. " Where does the fun come in?"

" Would you like to try a shot?" the Instructor asked.

"Oh—er—thanks," said Jones. "I've shot with a shot-gun, of course, but this "—he looked at the miniature rifle—" this isn't like a shot-gun, is it?"

"Not in the least," said the Friend. The Instructor passed Boy Jones a cartridge. The squad ceased firing and stared. Boy Jones reddened and fumbled.

"Hi! The beastly thing has slipped some-how!" he cried. The tiny twenty-two cartridge had dropped into the magazine-slot and stuck there, caught by the rim. The muzzle travelled vaguely round the horizon. The squad with one accord sat down on the dusty cement floor.

"Lend him a hair-pin," whispered the jobbing gardener.

"Muzzle *up*, please," said the Instructor (it was drooping towards the men on the floor). "I'll load for you. Now—keep her pointed towards the target—you're supposed to be firing at two hundred yards. Have you set your sights? Never mind, I'll set 'em. *Please* don't touch the trigger till you shoot."

Boy Jones was glistening at the edges as the Instructor swung him in the direction of the little targets fifty feet away. "Take a fine sight! The bull's eye should be just sitting on the top of the fore-sight," the Instructor cautioned. "Ah!"

Boy Jones, with a grunt and a jerk of the

shoulder, pulled the trigger. The right-hand window of the shed, six feet above the target, starred and cracked.

The boy who cleans the knives at the Vicarage buried his face in his hands; Jevons, the bricklayer's assistant, tied up his bootlace; the Fellow of the Royal Geographical Society looked at the roof; the village barber whistled softly. When one is twenty-two years old, and weighs twelve-stone-eight in hard condition, one does not approve of any game that one cannot play very well.

" I call this silly piffle," said Boy Jones, wiping his face.

" Oh, not so bad as that," said the Instructor. " We've all got to begin somehow. Try another?" But Boy Jones was not practising any more that afternoon. He seemed to need soothing.

" Come over to the big range," said the Friend. " You'll see the finished article at work down there. This is only for boys and beginners."

A knot of village lads from twelve to sixteen were scuffling for places on the shooting-mat as Boy Jones left the shed. On his way to the range, across the windy Downs, he preserved a silence foreign to his sunny nature. Jevons, the bricklayer's assistant, and the F.R.G.S. trotted past him—rifles at the carry.

" Awkward wind," said Jevons.   " Fish-tail!"

" What's a fish-tail?" said Boy Jones.

" Oh!   It means a fishy, tricky sort of a wind," said the Friend.   A shift in the uneasy north-east breeze brought them the far-away sob of a service rifle.

" For once in your young life," the Friend went on, " you're going to attend a game you do not understand."

" If you mean I'm expected to make an ass of myself again——" Boy Jones paused.

" Don't worry!   By this time I fancy Jevons will have told the Sergeant all about your performance in the shed just now.   *You* won't be pressed to shoot."

A long sweep of bare land opened before them. The thump of occasional shots grew clearer, and Boy Jones pricked his ears.

" What's that unholy whine and whop?" he asked in a lull of the wind.

" The whine is the bullet going across the valley.   The whop is when it hits the target— that white shutter thing sliding up and down against the hillside.   Those men lying down yonder are shooting at five hundred yards.   We'll look at 'em," said the Friend.

" This would make a thundering good golf-links," said Boy Jones, striding over the short, clean turf.   " Not a bad lie in miles of it."

" Yes, wouldn't it?" the Friend replied. " It would be even prettier as a croquet-lawn or a basket-ball pitch. Just the place for a picnic too. Unluckily, it's a rifle-range."

Boy Jones looked doubtful, but said nothing till they reached the five-hundred-yard butt. The Sergeant, on his stomach, binoculars to his eye, nodded, but not at the visitors. " Where did you sight, Walters?" he said.

" Nine o'clock—edge of the target," was the reply from a fat, blue man in a bowler hat, his trousers rucked half-way to his knees. " The wind's rotten bad down there!" He pointed towards the stiff-tailed wind-flags that stuck out at all sorts of angles as the eddy round the shoulder of the Down caught them.

" Let me try one," the Sergeant said, and reached behind him for a rifle.

" Hold on!" said the F.R.G.S. " That's Number Six. She throws high."

" She's *my* pet," said Jevons, holding out his hand for it. " Take Number Nine, Sergeant."

" Rifles are like bats, you know," the Friend explained. " They differ a lot."

The Sergeant sighted.

" He holds it steady enough," said Boy Jones.

" He mostly does," said the Friend. " If you watch that white disc come up you'll know it's a bull "

" Not much of one," said the Sergeant. " Too low—too far right. I gave her all the allowance I dared, too. That wind's funnelling badly in the valley. Give your wind-sight another three degrees, Walters."

The fat man's big fingers delicately adjusted the lateral sight. He had been firing till then by the light of his trained judgment, but some of the rifles were fitted with wind-gauges, and he wished to test one.

" What's he doing that for?" said Boy Jones.

" You wouldn't understand," said the Friend. " But take a squint along this rifle, and see what a bull looks like at five hundred yards. It isn't loaded, but don't point it at the pit of my stomach."

" Dash it all! I didn't *mean* to!" said Boy Jones.

" None of 'em mean it," the Friend replied. " That's how all the murders are done. Don't play with the bolt. Merely look along the sights. It isn't much of a mark, is it?"

" No, by Jove!" said Jones, and gazed with reverence at Walters, who announced before the marker had signalled his last shot that it was a likely heifer. (Walters was a butcher by profession.) A well-centred bull it proved to be.

" Now how the deuce did he do it?" said Boy Jones.

" By practice—first in the shed at two hundred

yards. We've five or six as good as him," said the Friend. "But he's not much of a snap-shooter when it comes to potting at dummy heads and shoulders exposed for five seconds. Jevons is our man then."

"Ah! talking of snap-shooting!" said the Sergeant, and—while Jevons fired his seven shots —delivered Boy Jones a curious little lecture on the advantages of the foggy English climate, the value of enclosed land for warfare, and the possi-bilities of well-directed small-arm fire wiping up —"spraying down" was his word—artillery, even in position.

"Well, I've got to go on and build houses," said Jevons. "Twenty-six is my score-card— sign please, Sergeant." He rose, dusted his knees, and moved off. His place was taken by a dark, cat-footed Coastguard, firing for the love of the game. He only ran to three cartridges, which he placed—magpie, five o'clock; inner, three o'clock; and bull. "Cordery don't take anything on trust," said the Sergeant. "He feels his way in to the bull every time. I like it. It's more rational."

While the F.R.G.S. was explaining to Boy Jones that the rotation of the earth on her axis affected a bullet to the extent of one yard in a thousand, a batch of six lads cantered over the hill.

"We're the new two-hundred-ers," they shouted.

"I know it," said the Sergeant. "Pick up the cartridge-cases; take my mackintosh and bag, and come on down to the two hundred range, quietly."

There was no need for the last caution. The boys picked up the things and swung off in couples—scout fashion.

"They are the survivors," the Friend explained, "of the boys you saw just now. They've passed their miniature rifle tests, and are supposed to be fit to fire in the open."

"And are they?" said Boy Jones, edging away from the F.R.G.S., who was talking about "jump" and "flip" in rifle-shooting.

"We'll see," said the Sergeant. "This wind ought to test 'em!"

Down in the hollow it rushed like a boulder-choked river, driving quick clouds across the sun: so that one minute, the eight-inch Bisley bull leaped forth like a headlight, and the next shrunk back into the grey-green grass of the butt like an engine backing up the line.

"Look here!" said the Sergeant, as the boys dropped into their places at the firing-point. "I warn you it's a three-foot wind on the target, *and* freshening. You'll get no two shots alike. Any boy that thinks he won't do himself justice can wait for a better day."

Nothing moved except one grin from face to face.

"No," said the Sergeant, after a pause.   "I don't suppose a thunder-storm would shift you young birds. Remember what I've been telling you all this spring.   Sighting shots, from the right!"

They went on one by one, carefully imitating the well-observed actions of their elders, even to the tapping of the cartridge on the rifle-butt. They scowled and grunted and compared notes as they set and reset their sights.   They brought up their rifles just as shadow gave place to sun, and, holding too long, fired when the cheating cloud returned.   It was unhappy, cold, nose-running, eye-straining work, but they enjoyed it passionately.   At the end they showed up their score-cards; one twenty-seven, two twenty-fives, a twenty-four, and two twenty-twos.   Boy Jones, his hands on his knees, had made no remark from first to last.

"Could I have a shot?" he began in a strangely meek voice.

But the chilled Sergeant had already whistled the marker out of the butt.   The wind-flags were being collected by the youngsters, and, with a tinkle of spent cartridge-cases returned to the Sergeant's bag, shooting ended.

"Not so bad," said the Sergeant.

"One of those boys was hump-backed," said

Boy Jones, with the healthy animal's horror of deformity.

"But his shots aren't," said the Sergeant. "He was the twenty-seven card.   Milligan's his name."

"I should like to have had a shot," Boy Jones repeated.   "Just for the fun of the thing."

"Well, just for the fun of the thing," the Friend suggested, "suppose you fill and empty a magazine.   Have you got any dummies, Sergeant?"

The Sergeant produced a handful of dummy cartridges from his inexhaustible bag.

"How d'you put 'em in?" said Boy Jones, picking up a cartridge by the bullet end with his left hand, and holding the rifle with his right.

"Here, Milligan," the Friend called.   "Fill and empty this magazine, will you, please?"

The cripple's fingers flickered for an instant round the rifle-breech.   The dummies vanished clicking.   He turned towards the butt, pausing perhaps a second on each aimed shot, ripped them all out again over his shoulder.   Mechanically Boy Jones caught them as they spun in the air; for he was a good fielder.

"Time, fifteen seconds," said the Friend. "You try now."   Boy Jones shook his head. "No, thanks," he said.   "This isn't my day out.   That's called magazine-fire, I suppose."

"Yes," said the Sergeant, "but it's more difficult to load in the dark or in a cramped position."

The boys drew off, larking among themselves. The others strolled homewards as the wind freshened. Only the Sergeant, after a word or two with the marker, struck off up the line of firing-butts.

"There seems to be a lot in it," said Boy Jones, after a while, to his friend. "But you needn't tell me," he went on in the tone of one ill at ease with himself, "don't tell *me* that when the hour strikes every man in England wouldn't —er—rally to the defence of his country like one man."

"And he'd be *so* useful while he was rallying, wouldn't he?" said the Friend shortly. "Imagine one hundred thousand chaps of your kidney introduced to the rifle for the first time, all loading and firing in your fashion! The hospitals wouldn't hold 'em!"

"Oh, there'd be time to get the general hang of the thing," said Boy Jones cheerily.

"When that hour strikes," the Friend replied, "it will already have struck, if you understand. There may be a few hours—perhaps ten or twelve — there will certainly not be more than a day and a night allowed us to get ready in."

"There will be six months at least," said Boy Jones confidently.

"Ah, you probably read that in a paper. I shouldn't rely on it, if I were you. It won't be like a county cricket match, date settled months in advance. By the way, are you playing for your county this season?"

Boy Jones seemed not to hear the last question. He had taken the Friend's rifle, and was idly clicking the bolt.

"Beg y' pardon, sir," said the Marker to the Friend in an undertone, "but the Sergeant's tryin' a gentleman's new rifle at nine hundred, and I'm waiting on for him. If you'd like to come into the trench?"—a discreet wink closed the sentence.

"Thanks awfully. That 'ud be quite interesting," said Boy Jones. The wind had dulled a little; the sun was still strong on the golden gorse; the Sergeant's straight back grew smaller and smaller as it moved away.

"You go down this ladder," said the Marker. They reached the raw line of the trench beneath the targets, the foot deep in the flinty chalk.

"Yes, sir," he went on, "here's where all the bullets ought to come. There's fourteen thousand of 'em this year, somewhere on the premises, but it don't hinder the rabbits from burrowing, just the same. *They* know shooting's

over as well as we do. You come here with a
shot-gun, and you won't see a single tail; but
they don't put 'emselves out for a rifle. Look,
there's the Parson!" He pointed at a bold,
black rabbit sitting half-way up the butt, who
loped easily away as the Marker ran up the large
nine-hundred-yard bull. Boy Jones stared at the
bullet-splintered framework of the targets, the
chewed edges of the woodwork, and the signifi-
cantly loosened earth behind them. At last he
came down, slowly it seemed, out of the sunshine,
into the chill of the trench. The marker opened
an old cocoa box, where he kept his paste and
paper patches.

"Things get mildewy down here," he explained. "Mr. Warren, our sexton, says it's
too like a grave to suit *him*. But as I say, it's
twice as deep and thrice as wide as what *he*
makes."

"I think it's rather jolly," said Boy Jones, and
looked up at the narrow strip of sky. The
Marker had quietly lowered the danger flag.
Something yowled like a cat with her tail trod on,
and a few fragments of pure white chalk crumbled
softly into the trench. Boy Jones jumped, and
flattened himself against the inner wall of the
trench. "The Sergeant is taking a sighting-
shot," said the Marker. "He must have hit a
flint in the grass somewhere. We can't comb

'em all out. The noise you noticed was the nickel envelope stripping, sir."

" But I didn't hear his gun go off," said Boy Jones.

" Not at nine hundred, with this wind, you wouldn't," said the Marker. " Stand on one side, please, sir. He's begun."

There was a rap overhead—a pause—down came the creaking target, up went the marking disc at the end of a long bamboo; a paper patch was slapped over the bullet hole, and the target slid up again, to be greeted with another rap, another, and another. The fifth differed in tone. " Here's a curiosity," said the Marker, pulling down the target. " The bullet must have ricochetted short of the butt, and it has key-holed, as we say. See!" He pointed to an ugly triangular rip and flap on the canvas target face. " If that had been flesh and blood, now," he went on genially, " it would have been just the same as running a plough up you. . . . Now he's on again!" The sixth rap was as thrillingly emphatic as one at a spiritualistic séance, but the seventh was followed by another yaa-ow of a bullet hitting a stone, and a tiny twisted sliver of metal fell at Boy Jones's rigid feet. He touched and dropped it. " Why, it's quite hot," he said.

" That's due to arrested motion," said the F.R.G.S. " Isn't it a funking noise, though?"

A pause of several minutes followed, during which they could hear the wind and the sea and the creaking of the Marker's braces.

" He said he'd finish off with a magazine full," the Marker volunteered. " I expect he's waiting for a lull in the wind. Ah! here it comes!"

It came—eleven shots slammed in at three-second intervals; a ricochet or two; one on the right-hand of the target's framework, which rang like a bell; a couple that hammered the old railway ties just behind the bull; and another that kicked a clod into the trench, and key-holed up the target. The others were various and scattering, but all on the butt.

" Sergeant can do better than that," said the Marker critically, overhauling the target. "It was the wind put him off, or (he winked once again), or . . . else he wished to show somebody something."

" I heard 'em all hit," said Boy Jones. " But I never heard the gun go off. Awful, I call it!"

" Well," said his friend, " it's the kind of bowling you'll have to face at forty-eight hours' notice—*if* you're lucky."

" It's the key-holing that I bar," said Boy Jones, following his own line of thought. The Marker put up his flag and ladder, and they climbed out of the trench into the sunshine.

" For pity's sake, look!" said the Marker, and stopped. " Well, well! If I 'adn't seen it, I wouldn't have credited it. You poor little impident fool. The Sergeant *will* be vexed."

"What has happened?" said Boy Jones, rather shrilly.

"He's killed the Parson, sir!" The Marker held up the still kicking body of a glossy black rabbit. One side of its head was not there.

"Talk of coin*ci*dence!" the Marker went on. "I know Sergeant 'll pretend he aimed for it. The poor little fool! Jumpin' about after his own businesses and thinking he was safe; and then to have his head fair mashed off him like this. Just look at him! Well! Well!"

It was anything but well with Boy Jones. He seemed sick.

*   *   *   *   *

A week later the Friend nearly stepped on him in the miniature-rifle shed. He was lying at length on the dusty coir matting, his trousers rucked half-way to his knees, his sights set as for two hundred, deferentially asking Milligan the cripple to stand behind him and tell him whether he was canting.

"No, you aren't now," said Milligan patronizingly, "but you were."

A DEPARTURE

Since first the White Horse Banner blew free,
  By Hengist's horde unfurled,
Nothing has changed on land or sea
  Of the things that steer the world.
(As it was when the long-ships scudded through the gale
  So it is where the Liners go.)
Time and Tide, they are both in a tale
  "Woe to the weaker—woe!"

No charm can bridle the hard-mouthed wind
  Or smooth the fretting swell.
No gift can alter the grey Sea's mind,
  But she serves the strong man well.
(As it is when her uttermost deeps are stirred
  So it is where the quicksands show,)
All the waters have but one word—
  "Woe to the weaker—woe!"

The feast is ended, the tales are told,
  The dawn is overdue,
And we meet on the quay in the whistling cold
  Where the galley waits her crew.
Out with the torches, they have flared too long,
  And bid the harpers go.
Wind and warfare have but one song—
  "Woe to the weaker—woe!"

Hail to the great oars gathering way,
  As the beach begins to slide!
Hail to the war-shields' click and play
  As they lift along our side!
Hail to the first wave over the bow—
  Slow for the sea-stroke!   Slow!—
All the benches are grunting now:—
  " *Woe to the weaker—woe!*"

THE BOLD 'PRENTICE

THE BOLD 'PRENTICE

This story is very much of the same sort as "An Unqualified Pilot," and shows that, when any one is really keen on his job, he will often find some older man who is even keener than he, who will give him help and instruction that could not be found in a whole library of books. Olaf Swanson's book of " Road-Locos Repair or the Young Driver's Vademecome," was well known in the Railway sheds in its day, and was written in the queerest English ever printed. But it told useful facts and, as you will see, saved a train at a pinch. It may be worth noticing that young Ottley's chance did not come to him till he had worked on and among engine-repairs for some five or six years and was well grounded in practical knowledge of his subject.

Young Ottley's father came to Calcutta in 1857 as fireman on the first locomotive ever run by the D.I.R., which was then the largest Indian railway. All his life he spoke broad Yorkshire, but young Ottley, being born in India, naturally talked the clipped sing-song that is used by the half-castes and English-speaking natives. When he was fifteen years old the D.I.R. took him into their service as an apprentice in the Locomotive Repair Department of the Ajaibpore workshops, and he became one of a gang of three or four white men and nine or ten natives.

There were scores of such gangs, each with its hoisting and overhead cranes, jack-screws, vices and lathes, as separate as separate shops, and their work was to mend locomotives and make the apprentices behave. But the apprentices threw nuts at one another, chalked caricatures of unpopular foremen on buffer-bars and discarded boilers, and did as little work as they possibly could.

They were nearly all sons of old employees, living with their parents in the white bungalows of Steam Road or Church Road or Albert Road— on the broad avenues of pounded brick bordered by palms and crotons and bougainvilleas and bamboos which made up the railway town of Ajaibpore. They had never seen the sea or a steamer; half their speech was helped out with native slang; they were all volunteers in the D.I.R.'s Railway Corps—grey with red facings— and their talk was exclusively about the Company and its affairs.

They all hoped to become engine-drivers earning six or eight hundred a year, and therefore they despised all mere sit-down clerks in the Store, Audit and Traffic departments, and ducked them when they met at the Company's swimming baths.

There were no strikes or tie-ups on the D.I.R. in those days, for the reason that the ten or twelve thousand natives and two or three thousand whites were doing their best to turn the Company's employment into a caste in which their sons and relatives would be sure of positions and pensions. Everything in India crystallizes into a caste sooner or later—the big jute and cotton mills, the leather, harness and opium factories, the coal-mines and the dockyards, and, in years to come, when India begins to be heard from as one of the manufacturing countries of the world, the labour Unions of other lands will learn something about the beauty of caste which will greatly interest them.

Those were the days when the D.I.R. decided that it would be cheaper to employ native drivers as much as possible, and the " Sheds," as they called the Repair Department, felt the change acutely; for a native driver could misuse his engine, they said, more curiously than any six monkeys. The Company had not then standardized its rolling-stock, and this was very good for apprentices anxious to learn about machines, because there were, perhaps, twenty types of locomotives in use on the road. They were Hawthornes; E types; O types; outside cylinders; Spaulding and Cushman double-enders and short-run Continental-built tank engines, and many others. But the native drivers burned them all out impartially, and the apprentices took to writing remarks in Bengali on the cabs of the repaired ones where the next driver would be sure to see them.

Young Ottley worked at first as little as the other apprentices, but his father, who was then a pensioned driver, taught him a great deal about the insides of locomotives; and Olaf Swanson, the red-headed Swede who ran the Government Mail, the big Thursday express, from Serai Rajgara to Guldee Haut, was a great friend of the Ottley family, and dined with them every Friday night.

Olaf was an important person, for besides being the best of the mail-drivers, he was Past Master of the big railway Masonic Lodge, " St. Duncan's in the East," Secretary of the Drivers' Provident Association, a Captain in the D.I.R. Volunteer Corps, and, which he thought much more of, an Author; for he had written a book in a language of his own which he insisted upon calling English, and had printed it at his own expense at the ticket-printing works.

Some of the copies were buff and green, and some were pinkish and blue, and some were yellow and brown; for Olaf did not believe in wasting money on high-class white paper. Wrapping-paper was good enough for him, and besides, he said the colours rested the eyes of the reader.   It was called " The Art of Road-Locos Repair or The Young Driver's Vademecome," and was dedicated in verse to a man of the name of Swedenborg.

It covered every conceivable accident that could happen to an engine on the road; and gave a rough-and-ready remedy for each; but you had to understand Olaf's written English, as well as all the technical talk about engines, to make head or tail of it, and you had also to know personally every engine on the D.I.R., for the " Vademecome " was full of what might be called " locomotive allusions," which concerned the D.I.R. only.   Otherwise, it would, as some great locomotive designer once said, have been a classic and a text-book.

Olaf was immensely proud of it, and would pin young Ottley in a corner and make him learn whole pages—it was written all in questions and answers—by heart.

" Never mind what she *means*," Olaf would shout.   " You learn her word-perfect, and she will help you in the Sheds.   I drive the Mail,— *the* mail of all India,—and what I write and say is true."

" But I do *not* wish to learn the book," said young Ottley, who thought he saw quite enough of locomotives in business hours.

" You *shall* learn!   I haf great friendship for

your father, and so I shall teach you whether you like it or not."

Young Ottley submitted, for he was really fond of old Olaf, and at the end of six months' teaching in Olaf's peculiar way began to see that the "Vademecome" was a very valuable help in the repair sheds, when broken-down engines of a new type came in. Olaf gave him a copy bound in cartridge paper and hedged round the margins with square-headed manuscript notes, each line the result of years of experience and accidents.

"There is nothing in this book," said Olaf, "that I have not tried in my time, and I say that the engine is like the body of a man. So long as there is steam—the life, you see,—so long, if you know how, you can make her move a little,—so!" He waggled his hand slowly. "Till a man is dead or the engine she is at the bottom of a river, you can do something with her. Remember that! *I* say it and I know."

He repaid young Ottley's time and attention by using his influence to get him made a Sergeant in his Company, and young Ottley, being a keen Volunteer and a good shot, stood well with the D.I.R. in the matter of casual leave. When repairs were light in the Sheds and the honour of the D.I.R. was to be upheld at some far-away station against the men of Agra or Bandikui, the narrow-gauge railway-towns of the west, young

Ottley would contrive to get away, and help to uphold it on the glaring dusty rifle-ranges of those parts.

A 'prentice never dreamed of paying for his ticket on any line in India, least of all when he was in uniform, and young Ottley was practically as free of the Indian railway system as any member of the Supreme Legislative Council who wore a golden General Pass on his watch-chain and could ride where he chose.

Late in September of his nineteenth year he went north on one of his cup-hunting excursions, elegantly and accurately dressed, with one-eighth of one inch of white collar showing above his grey uniform stock and his Martini-Henry rifle polished to match his sergeant's sword in the rack above him.

The rains were out, and in Bengal that means a good deal to the railways; for the rain falls for three months lavishly, till the whole country is one sea, and the snakes take refuge on the embankment, and the racing floods puff out the brick ballast from under the iron ties, and leave the rails hanging in graceful loops. Then the trains run as they can, and the permanent-way inspectors spend their nights flourishing about in hand-carts pushed by coolies over the dislocated metals, and everybody is covered with the fire-red rash of prickly heat, and loses his temper.

Young Ottley was used to these things from

birth.   All he regretted was that his friends along the line were so draggled and dripping and sulky that they could not appreciate his gorgeousness; for he considered himself very consoling to behold when he cocked his helmet over one eye and puffed the rank smoke of native-made cigars through his nostrils.   Until night fell he lay out on his bunk, in his shirt sleeves, reading the works of G. W. R. Reynolds, which were sold on all the railway bookstalls, and dozing at intervals.

Then he found they were changing engines at Guldee Haut, and old Rustomjee, a Parsee, was the new driver, with Number Forty in hand. Young Ottley took this opportunity to go forward and tell Rustomjee exactly what they thought of him in the Sheds, where the 'prentices had been repairing some of his carelessness in the way of a dropped crown-sheet, the result of inattention and bad stoking.

Rustomjee said he had bad luck with engines, and young Ottley went back to his carriage and slept.   He was waked by a bang, a bump, and a jar, and saw on the opposite bunk a subaltern who was travelling north with a detachment of some twenty English soldiers.

" What's that?" said the subaltern.

" Rustomjee has blown her up, perhaps," said young Ottley, and dropped out into the wet, the subaltern at his heels.   They found Rustomjee sitting by the side of the line, nursing a scalded foot and crying aloud that he was a dead man, while the gunner-guard—who is a kind of extra-hand—looked respectfully at the roaring, hissing machine.

" What has happened?" said young Ottley, by the light of the gunner-guard's lantern.

" *Phut gya* [She has gone smash]," said Rustomjee, still hopping.

" Without doubt; but where?"

" *Khuda jahnta!* [God knows].   I am a poor man.   Number Forty is broke."

Young Ottley jumped into the cab and turned off all the steam he could find, for there was a good deal escaping.   Then he took the lantern and dived under the drive-wheels, where he lay face up, investigating among spurts of hot water.

" Doocid plucky," said the subaltern.   " *I* shouldn't like to do that myself.   What's gone wrong?"

" Cylinder-head blown off, coupler-rod twisted, and several more things.   She is very badly wrecked.   Oah, yes, she is a tottal wreck," said young Ottley between the spokes of the right-hand driver.

" Awkward," said the subaltern, turning up his coat-collar in the wet.   " What's to be done, then?"

Young Ottley came out, a rich black all over

his grey uniform with the red facings, and drummed on his teeth with his finger-nails, while the rain fell and the native passengers shouted questions and old Rustomjee told the gunner-guard to walk back six or seven miles and wire to some one for help.

"I cannot swim," said the gunner-guard. "Go and lie down." And that, as you might say, settled that. Besides, as far as one could see by the light of the gunner-guard's lantern, all Bengal was flooded.

"Olaf Swanson will be at Serai Rajgara with the Mail. He will be particularly angry," said young Ottley. Then he ducked under the engine again with a flare-lamp and sat cross-legged, considering things and wishing he had brought his " Vademecome " in his valise.

Number Forty was an old reconstructed Mutiny engine, with Frenchified cock-nosed cylinders and a profligate allowance of under-pinning. She had been through the Sheds several times, and young Ottley, though he had never worked on her, had heard much about her, but nothing to her credit.

"You can lend me some men?" he said at last to the subaltern. "Then I think we shall dis-connect her this side, and perhaps, notwithstand-ing, she will move. We will try—eh?"

"Of course we will. Hi! Sergeant!" said

the subaltern.   " Turn out the men here and do
what this—this officer tells you."

" Officer!" said one of the privates, under his
breath.   " 'Didn't think I'd enlisted to serve
under a Sergeant o' Volunteers.   'Ere's a 'orrible
street accident.   'Looks like mother's tea-kettle
broke.   What d'yer expect us to do, Mister
Civilian Sergeant?"

Young Ottley explained his plan of campaign
while he was ravaging Rustomjee's tool-chest, and
then the men crawled and knelt and levered and
pushed and hauled and turned spanners under the
engine, as young Ottley told them.   What he
wanted was to disconnect the right cylinder altogether, and get off a badly twisted coupler-rod.
Practically Number Forty's right side was
paralysed, and they pulled away enough iron-
mongery there to build a culvert with.

Young Ottley remembered that the instructions for a case like this were all in the " Vademecome," but even he began to feel a little alarmed
as he saw what came away from the engine and
was stacked by the side of the line.   After forty
minutes of the hardest kind of work it seemed to
him that everything movable was cleared out, and
that he might venture to give her steam.   She
leaked and sweated and shook, but she moved—
in a grinding sort of way—and the soldiers
cheered.

Rustomjee flatly refused to help in anything so revolutionary as driving an engine on one cylinder, because, he said, Heaven had decreed that he should always be unlucky, even with sound machines. Moreover, as he pointed out, the pressure-gauge was jumping up and down like a bottle-imp. The stoker had long since gone away into the night; for he was a prudent man.

" Doocid queer thing altogether," said the subaltern, " but look here, if you like, I'll chuck on the coals and you can drive the old jigamaroo, if she'll go."

" Perhaps she will blow up," said the gunner-guard.

" 'Shouldn't at all wonder by the sound of her. Where's the shovel?" said the subaltern.

" Oah no. She's all raight according to my book, I think," said young Ottley. " Now we will go to Serai Rajgara—if she moves."

She moved with long *ssghee*! *ssghee's*! of exhaustion and lamentation. She moved quite seven miles an hour, and—for the floods were all over the line—the staggering voyage began.

The subaltern stoked four shovels to the minute, spreading them thin, and Number Forty made noises like a dying cow, and young Ottley discovered that it was one thing to run a healthy switching-locomotive up and down the yards for fun when the head of the yard wasn't looking,

and quite another to drive a very sick one over
an unknown road in absolute darkness and tropic
rain.   But they felt their way along with their
hearts in their mouths till they came to a distant
signal, and whistled frugally, having no steam to
spare.

"This *might* be Serai Rajgara," said young
Ottley, hopefully.

"'Looks more like the Suez Canal," said the
subaltern.   "I say, when an engine kicks up that
sort of a noise she's a little impatient, isn't she?"

"That sort of noise" was a full-powered,
furious yelling whistle half a mile up the line.

"That is the Down Mail," said young Ottley.
"We have delayed Olaf two hours and forty-five
minutes.   She must surely be in Serai Rajgara."

"'Don't wonder she wants to get out of it,"
said the subaltern.   "Golly, what a country!"

The line here dipped bodily under water, and
young Ottley sent the gunner-guard on to find
the switch to let Number Forty into the siding.
Then he followed and drew up with a doleful
wop! wop! wop! by the side of the great forty-
five-ton, six-wheel, coupled, eighteen-inch inside-
cylinder Number Twenty-five, all paint and
lacquer, standing roaring at the head of the Down
Mail.   The rest was all water—flat, level and
solid from one point of the horizon to the other.

Olaf's red beard flared like a danger-signal,

P

and as soon as they were in range some knobby pieces of Giridih coal whizzed past young Ottley's head.

" 'Your friend very mad?" said the subaltern, ducking.

" Aah!" roared Olaf. " This is the fifth time you make delay. Three hours' delay you make *me*—Swanson—the Mail! Now I will lose more time to break your head." He swung on to the foot-board of Number Forty, with a shovel in one hand.

" Olaf!" cried young Ottley, and Olaf nearly tumbled backward. " Rustomjee is behind."

" Of course. He always is. But you? How you come here?"

" Oah, we smashed up. I have disconnected her and arrived here on one cylinder, by your book. We are only a—a diagram of an engine, I think."

" My book! My very good book! My ' Vademecome '! Ottley, you are a fine driver. I forgive my delays. It was worth. Oh, my book, my book!" and Olaf leapt back to Number Twenty-five, shouting things about Swedenborg and steam.

" Thatt is all right," said young Ottley, " but where is Serai Rajgara? We want assistance."

" There is no Serai Rajgara. The water is two feet on the embankment, and the telegraph office

is fell in.   I will report at Purnool Road.   Good-
night, good boy!"

The Mail train splashed out into the dark, and
Ottley made great haste to let off his steam and
draw his fire.   Number Forty had done enough
for that night.

" Odd chap, that friend of yours," said the
subaltern, when Number Forty stood empty and
disarmed in the gathering waters.   " What do
we do now?   Swim?"

" Oah, no!   At ten-forty-five thiss morning
that is coming, an engine will perhaps arrive from
Purnool Road and take us north.   Now we will
lie down and go to sleep.   You see there *is* no
Serai Rajgara.   You could get a cup of tea here
once on a time."

" Oh, my Aunt, what a country!" said the
subaltern, as he followed Ottley to the carriage
and lay down on the leather bunk.

For the next three weeks Olaf Swanson talked
to everybody of nothing but his " Vademecome "
and young Ottley.   What he said about his book
does not matter, but the compliments of a mail-
driver are things to be repeated, as they were, to
people in high authority, the masters of many
engines.   So young Ottley was sent for, and he
came from the Sheds buttoning his jacket and
wondering which of his sins had been found out
this time.

It was a loop line near Ajaibpore, where he
could by no possibility come to harm. It was
light but steady traffic, and a first-class superintendent was in charge; but it was a driver's
billet, and permanent after six months. As a
new engine was on order for the loop, the fore-
man of the Sheds told young Ottley he might
look through the stalls and suit himself.

He waited, boiling with impatience, till Olaf
came in, and the two went off together, old Olaf
clucking, " Look! Look! Look!" like a hen,
all down the Sheds, and they chose a nearly new
Hawthorne, No. 239, which Olaf highly recom-
mended. Then Olaf went away, to give young
Ottley his chance to order her to the cleaning-pit,
and jerk his thumb at the cleaner and say, as he
turned magnificently on his heel, " Thursday,
eight o'clock. *Mallum?* 'Understand?'"

That was almost the proudest moment of his
life. The very proudest was when he pulled out
of Atami Junction through the brick-field on the
way to his loop, and passed the Down Mail, with
Olaf in the cab.

They say in the Sheds that you could have
heard Number Two hundred and Thirty-nine's
whistle from Raneegunge clear to Calcutta.

THE NURSES

When, with a pain he desires to explain to the multitude,
    Baby howls
Himself black in the face, toothlessly striving to curse;
And the six-months-old Mother begins to enquire of the
    Gods if it may be
Tummy, or Temper, or Pins—what does the adequate
    Nurse?

See!   At one turn of her head the trouble is guessed;
    and, thereafter,
She juggles (unscared by his throes) with drops of hot
    water and spoons,
Till the hiccoughs are broken by smiles, and the smiles
    pucker up into laughter,
And he lies o'er her shoulder and crows, and she, as she
    nurses him, croons!

When, at the head of the grade, tumultuous out of the
    cutting,
Pours the belated Express, roars at the night, and draws
    clear,
Redly obscured or displayed by her fire-door's opening
    and shutting—
Symbol of strength under stress—what does her small
    engineer?

Clamour and darkness encircle his way.   Do they deafen
    or blind him?
No!—nor the pace he must keep.   He, being used to
    these things,
Placidly follows his work, which is laying his mileage
    behind him,
While his passengers trustfully sleep, and he, as he handles
    her, sings!

When, with the gale at her heel, the barque lies down
    and recovers—
Rolling through forty degrees, combing the stars with her
    tops,
What says the man at the wheel, holding her straight as
    she hovers
On the summits of wind-screening seas, steadying her as
    she drops?

Behind him the blasts without check from the Pole to the
    Tropic, pursue him,
Heaving up, heaping high, slamming home, the surges he
    must not regard:
Beneath him the crazy wet deck, and all Ocean on end
    to undo him;
Above him one desperate sail, thrice-reefed but still
    buckling the yard!

Under his hand fleet the spokes and return, to be held or
    set free again;
And she bows and makes shift to obey their behest, till
    the master-wave comes

And her gunnel goes under in thunder and smokes, and
    she chokes in the trough of the sea again—
Ere she can lift and make way to its crest; and he, as he
    nurses her, hums!

These have so utterly mastered their work that they work
    without thinking;
Holding three-fifths of their brain in reserve for whatever
    betide.
So, when catastrophe threatens, of colic, collision or sinking,
They shunt the full gear into train, and take the small thing
    in their stride.

THE SON OF HIS FATHER

THE SON OF HIS FATHER

" It is a queer name," Mrs. Strickland admitted,
" and none of our family have ever borne it; but,
you see, he *is* the first man to us."

So he was called Adam, and to that world
about him he was the first of men—a man-child
alone. Heaven sent him no Eve for a companion, but all earth, horse and foot, was at his
feet. As soon as he was old enough to appear in
public he held a levée, and Strickland's sixty
policemen, with their sixty clanking sabres, bowed
to the dust before him. When his fingers closed
a little on Imam Din's sword-hilt they rose and
roared till Adam roared too, and was withdrawn.

" Now that was no cry of fear," said Imam Din
afterwards, speaking to his companion in the
Police lines. " He was angry—and so young!
Brothers, he will make a very strong Police
officer."

" Does the Memsahib nurse him?" said a new
recruit, the dye-smell not yet out of his yellow
cotton uniform.

"Ho!" said an up-country Naik scornfully; "it has not been known for *more* than ten days that my woman nurses him." He curled his moustaches as lordly as ever an Inspector could afford to do, for he knew that the husband of the foster-mother of the son of the District Superintendent of Police was a man of consideration.

"I am glad," said Imam Din, loosening his belt. "Those who drink our blood become of our own blood, and I have seen, in those thirty years, that the sons of Sahibs once being born here return when they are men. Yes, they return after they have been to Belait [Europe]."

"And what do they in Belait?" asked the recruit respectfully.

"Get instruction—which thou hast not," returned the Naik. "Also they drink of *belaitee-panee* [soda-water] enough to give them that devil's restlessness which endures for all their lives. Whence we of Hind have trouble."

"My father's uncle," said Imam Din slowly, with importance, "was Ressaldar of the Long Coat Horse; and the Empress called him to Europe in the year that she had accomplished fifty years of rule. *He* said (and there were also other witnesses) that the Sahibs there drink only common water even as do we; and that the *belaitee-panee* does *not* run in all their rivers."

"He said that there was a Shish Mahal—a

glass palace—half a mile in length, and that the rail-train ran under roads; and that there are boats bigger than a village.   He is a great talker." The Naik spoke scornfully.   He had no well-born uncles.

" *He* is at least a man of good birth," said Imam Din, and the Naik was silent.

" Ho!   Ho!"   Imam Din reached out to his pipe, chuckling till his fat sides shook again. " Strickland Sahib's foster-mother was the wife of a gardener in the Ferozepur district.   I was a young man then.   This child also will be suckled here and he will have double wisdom, and when he is a Police officer it will be very bad for the thieves in this part of the world.   Ho!   Ho!"

" Strickland Sahib's butler has said," the Naik went on, " that they will call him Adam—and no jaw-splitting English name.   Udaam.   The *padre* will name him at their church in due time."

" Who can tell the ways of Sahibs?   Now Strickland Sahib knows more of the Faith than ever I had time to learn—prayers, charms, names and stories of the Blessed Ones.   Yet he is not a Mussulman," said Imam Din thoughtfully.

" For the reason that he knows as much of the gods of Hindustan, and so he rides with a rein in each hand.   Remember that he sat under the Baba Atal, a *faquir* among *faquirs*, for ten days;

whereby a man came to be hanged for the murder
of a dancing girl on the night of the great earth-
quake," the Naik replied.

"True—it is true.   And yet—the Sahibs are
one day so wise—and another so foolish.   But
he has named the child well; Adam.   Huzrut
Adam.   Ho!   Ho!   Father Adam we must call
him."

"And all who minister to the child," said the
Naik quietly, but with meaning, "will come to
great honour."

Adam throve, being prayed over before the
Gods of at least three creeds, in a garden almost
as fair as Eden.   There were gigantic clumps of
bamboos that talked continually, and enormous
plantains, trees on whose soft, paper skin he could
scratch with his nails;   green domes of mango-
trees as huge as the dome of St. Paul's, full of
parrots as big as cassowaries and grey squirrels
the size of foxes.   At the end of the garden stood
a hedge of flaming poinsettias higher than anything in the world, because, child-like, Adam's
eye could not carry to the tops of the mango-trees.
Their green went out against the blue sky, but
the red poinsettias he could just see.   A nurse
who talked continually about snakes and pulled
him back from the mouth of a fascinating dry
well, and a mother who believed that the sun hurt
little heads, were the only drawbacks to this loveli-

ness. But, as his legs grew under him, he found that by scaling an enormous rampart—three feet of broken-down mud wall at the end of the garden—he could come into a ready-made kingdom, where every one was his slave. Imam Din showed him the way one evening, and the Police troopers, cooking their supper, received him with rapture, and gave him pieces of very indigestible, but altogether delightful, spiced bread.

Here he sat or sprawled in the horse-feed where the Police were picketed in a double line, and he named them, men and beasts together, according to his ideas and experiences, as his First Father had done before him.   In those days everything had a name, from the mud mangers to the heel-ropes, for things were people to Adam exactly as people are things to folk in their second childhood. Through all the conferences—one hand twisted into Imam Din's beard, and the other on his polished belt buckle—there were two other people who came and went across the talk —Death and Sickness—persons greater than Imam Din, and stronger than the heel-roped horses.   There was Mata, the small-pox, a woman in some way connected with pigs; and Heza, the cholera, a black man, according to Adam; and Booka, starvation; and Kismet, who settled all questions, from the untimely choking of a pet

mungoose in the kitchen-drain to the absence of
a young Policeman who once missed a parade and
never came back. It was all very wonderful to
Adam, but not worth much thinking over; for
a child's mind is bounded by his eyes exactly as
a horse's view of the road is limited by his blinkers.
Between all these objectionable shadowy vagrants
stood a ring of kind faces and strong arms, and
Mata and Heza would never touch Adam, the
first of men. Kismet might do so, because—and
this was a mystery no staring into his looking-
glass would solve—Kismet was written, like
Police orders for the day, in or on Adam's head.
Imam Din could not explain how this might be,
and it was from that grey, fat Mohammedan that
Adam learned through every inflection the *Khuda
jhanta* [God knows!] that settles everything in
the mind of Asia.

Beyond the fact that " Khuda " [God] was a
very good man and kept lions, Adam's theology
did not run far. Mrs. Strickland tried to teach
him a few facts, but he revolted at the story of
Genesis as untrue. A turtle, he said, upheld the
world, and one-half the adventures of Huzrut Nu
[Father Noah] had never been told. If Mamma
wanted to hear them she must ask Imam Din.

" It's awful," said Mrs. Strickland, half crying,
" to think of his growing up like a little heathen."
Mrs. Strickland had been born and brought up

in England, and did not quite understand Eastern
things.

"Let him alone," said Strickland. "He'll
grow out of it all, or it will only come back to
him in dreams."

"Are you sure?" said his wife.

"Quite. I was sent home when I was seven,
and they flicked it out of me with a wet towel at
Harrow. Public schools don't encourage anything that isn't quite English."

Mrs. Strickland shuddered, for she had been
trying not to think of the separation that follows
motherhood in India, and makes life there, for
all that is written to the contrary, not quite
the most desirable thing in the world. Adam
trotted out to hear about more miracles, and his
nurse must have worried him beyond bounds,
for she came back weeping, saying that Adam
Baba was in danger of being eaten alive by wild
horses.

As a matter of fact he had shaken off Juma by
bolting between a couple of picketed horses, and
lying down under their bellies. That they were
old personal friends of his, Juma did not understand, nor Strickland either. Adam was settled
at ease when his father arrived, breathless and
white, and the stallions put back their ears and
squealed.

"If you come here," said Adam, "they will

Q

hit you kicks.   Tell Juma I have eaten my rice, and I wish to be alone."

" Come out at once," said Strickland, for the horses were beginning to paw.

" Why should I obey Juma's order?   She is afraid of horses."

" It is not Juma's order.   It is mine.   Obey!"

" Ho!" said Adam.   " Juma did not tell me that "; and he crawled out on all-fours among the shod feet.   Mrs. Strickland was crying bitterly with fear and excitement, and as a sacrifice to the home gods Adam had to be whipped.   He said with perfect justice—

" There was no order that I should *not* sit with the horses, and they are *my* horses.   Why is there this *tamasha* [fuss]?"

Strickland's face showed him that the whipping was coming, and the child turned white.   Mother-like, Mrs. Strickland left the room, but Juma, the foster-mother, stayed to see.

" Am I to be whipped here?" he gasped.

" Of course."

" Before that woman?   Father, I am a man— I am not afraid.   It is my *izzat*—my honour."

Strickland only laughed—(to this day I cannot imagine what possessed him), and gave Adam the little tap-tap with a riding cane that was whipping sufficient for his years.

When it was all over, Adam said quietly, " I

am little and you are big. If I had stayed among my horse-folk I should not have been whipped. *You* are afraid to go there."

The merest chance led me to Strickland's house that afternoon. When I was half-way down the drive Adam passed me without recognition, at a fast run. I caught one glimpse of his face under his big hat, and it was the face of his father as I had once seen it in the grey of the morning when it bent over a leper. I caught the child by the shoulder.

" Let me go!" he screamed; though he and I were the best of friends, as a rule. " Let me go!"

" Where to, Father Adam?" He was quivering like a haltered colt.

" To the well. I have been beaten. I have been beaten before a woman! Let me go!" He tried to bite my hand.

" That is a small matter," I said. " Men are born to beatings."

" *Thou* hast never been beaten," he said savagely (we were talking in the native tongue).

" Indeed I have; times past counting."

" Before women?"

" My mother and my ayah saw. *By* women, too, for that matter. What of it?"

" What didst thou do?" He stared beyond my shoulder up the long drive.

" It is long ago, and I have forgotten. I was older than thou art ; but even then I forgot, and now the thing is only a jest to be talked of."

Adam drew one big breath and broke down utterly in my arms. Then he raised his head, and his eyes were Strickland's eyes when Strickland gave orders.

" Ho! Imam Din!"

The fat orderly seemed to spring out of the earth at our feet, crashing through the bushes, and standing at attention.

" Hast *thou* ever been beaten?" said Adam.

" Assuredly. By my father when I was thirty years old. He beat me with a plough-beam before all the women of the village."

" Wherefore?"

" Because I had returned to the village on leave from the Government service, and said of the village elders that they had not seen the world. Therefore he beat me to show that no seeing of the world changes father and son."

" And thou?"

" I stood up to the beating. He was my father."

" Good," said Adam, and turned on his heel without another word.

Imam Din looked after him. " An elephant breeds but once in a lifetime, but he breeds elephants. Yet, I am glad I am no father of tuskers," said he.

" What is it all?" I asked.

" His father beat him with a whip no bigger than a reed. But the child could not have done what he desired to do without leaping through me. And I am of some few pounds weight. Look!"

Imam Din stepped back through the bushes, and the pressed grass showed that he had been lying curled round the mouth of the dry well.

" When there was talk of beating, I knew that one who sat among horses such as ours was not like to kiss his father's hand. He might have done away with himself. So I lay down in this place." We stood still looking at the well-curb.

Adam came along the garden path to us. " I have spoken to my father," he said simply. " Imam Din, tell thy Naik that his woman is dismissed my service."

" *Huzoor!* [Your Highness!]" said Imam Din, stooping low.

" For no fault of hers."

" Protector of the Poor!"

" And to-day."

" *Khodawund!* [Heaven-born!]"

" It is an order. Go!"

Again the salute, and Imam Din departed, with that same set of the back which he wore when he had taken an order from Strickland. I thought that it would be well to go too, but Strickland beckoned me from the verandah. When I came up he was perfectly white, rocking to and fro in his chair.

" Do you know he was going to chuck himself down the well—because I tapped him just now?" he said helplessly.

" I ought to," I replied. " He has just dismissed his nurse—on his own authority, I suppose?"

" He told me just now that he wouldn't have her for a nurse any more. I never supposed he meant it for an instant. I suppose she'll have to go."

Now Strickland, the Police officer, was feared through the length and breadth of the Punjab by murderers, horse-thieves, and cattle-lifters.

Adam returned, halting outside the verandah.

" I have sent Juma away because she saw that —that which happened. Until she is gone I do not come into the house," he said.

" But to send away thy foster-mother!" said Strickland with reproach.

" *I* do not send her away. It is *thy* blame," and the small forefinger was pointed to Strickland. " I will not obey her. I will not eat from her hand. I will not sleep with her. Send her away!"

Strickland stepped out and lifted the child into the verandah.

" This folly has lasted long enough," he said. " Come now and be wise."

" I am little and you are big," said Adam between set teeth. " You can beat me before this man or cut me to pieces. But I will *not* have Juma for my ayah any more. She saw me beaten. I will not eat till she goes. I swear it by—my father's head."

Strickland sent him indoors to his mother, and we could hear sounds of weeping and Adam's voice saying nothing more than " Send Juma away!" Presently Juma came in and wept too, and Adam repeated, " It is no fault of thine, but go!"

And the end of it was that Juma went with all her belongings, and Adam fought his own way into his little clothes until the new ayah came. His address of welcome to her was rather amazing. In a few words it ran: " If I do wrong, send me to my father. If you strike me, I will try to kill you. I do not wish my ayah to play with me. Go and eat rice!"

From that Adam forswore the society of ayahs and small native boys as much as a small boy can, confining himself to Imam Din and his friends of the Police. The Naik, Juma's husband, had been presuming not a little on his position, and when Adam's favour was withdrawn from his wife he thought it best to apply for a transfer to another post. There were too many companions anxious to report his shortcomings to Strickland.

Towards his father Adam kept a guarded neutrality. There was not a touch of sulkiness in it, for the child's temper was as clear as a bell. But the difference and the politeness worried Strickland.

If the Policemen had loved Adam before the affair of the well, they worshipped him now.

" He knows what honour means," said Imam Din. " He has justified himself upon a point thereof. He has carried an order through his father's household as a child of the Blood might do. Therefore he is not altogether a child any longer. Wah! He is a tiger's cub." The next time that Adam made his little unofficial inspection of the lines, Imam Din, and, by consequence, all the others, stood upon their feet with their hands to their sides, instead of calling out from where they lay, " Salaam, Babajee," and other disrespectful things.

But Strickland took counsel with his wife, and she with the cheque-book and their lean bank account, and they decided that Adam must go " home " to his aunts. But England is not home to a child who has been born in India, and it never becomes home-like unless he spends all his youth there.   Their bank-book showed that if they economized through the summer by going to a cheap hill-station instead of to Simla (where Mrs. Strickland's parents lived, and where Strickland might be noticed by the Government) they could send Adam home in the next spring. It would be hard pinching, but it could be done.

Dalhousie was chosen as being the cheapest of the hill-stations;—Dalhousie and a little five-roomed cottage full of mildew, tucked away among the rhododendrons.

Adam had been to Simla three or four times, and knew by name most of the drivers on the road there, but this new place disquieted him. He came to me for information, his hands deep in his knickerbocker pockets, walking step for step as his father walked.

" There will be none of my *bhai-bund* [brother-hood] up there," he said disconsolately, " and they say that I must lie still in a doolie [palan-quin] for a day and a night, being carried like a sheep.   I wish to take some of my mounted men to Dalhousie."

I told him that there was a small boy, called Victor, at Dalhousie, who had a calf for a pet, and was allowed to play with it on the public roads.   After that Adam could not sufficiently hurry the packing.

" First," said he, " I shall ask that man Victor to let me play with the cow's child. If he is *muggra* [ill-conditioned], I shall tell my Policemen to take it away."

" But that is unjust," said Strickland, " and there is no order that the Police should do injustice."

" When the Government pay is not sufficient, and low-caste men are promoted, what *can* an honest man do?" Adam replied, in the very touch and accent of Imam Din; and Strickland's eyebrows went up.

" You talk too much to the Police, my son," he said.

" Always. About everything," said Adam promptly. " They say that when I am an officer I shall know as much as my father."

" God forbid, little one!"

" They say, too, that you are as clever as Shaitan [the Evil One], to know things."

" They say that, do they?" and Strickland looked pleased. His pay was small, but he had his reputation, and it was dear to him.

" They say also—not to me, but to one another when they eat rice behind the wall—that in your own heart you esteem yourself as wise as Suleiman [Solomon], who was cheated by Shaitan."

This time Strickland did not look so pleased. Adam, in all innocence, launched into a long story about Suleiman-bin-Daoud, who once, out of vanity, pitted his wits against Shaitan, and because God was not on his side Shaitan sent " a little devil of low caste," as Adam put it, who cheated him utterly and put him to shame before " all the other Kings."

" By Gum!" said Strickland, when the tale was done, and went away, while Adam took me to task for laughing at Imam Din's stories. I did not wonder that he was called Huzrut Adam, for he looked old as all time in his grave child-hood, sitting cross-legged, his battered little helmet far at the back of his head, his forefinger wagging up and down, native fashion, and the wisdom of serpents on his unconscious lips.

That May he went up to Dalhousie with his mother, and in those days the journey ended in fifty or sixty miles of uphill travel in a doolie or palanquin along a road winding through the Himalayas. Adam sat in the doolie with his mother, and Strickland rode and tied with me, a spare doolie following. The march began after we got out of the train at Pathankot, in a wet hot night among the rice and poppy fields.

II

It was all new to Adam, and he had opinions to advance—notably about a fish that jumped in a wayside pond. "*Now* I know," he shouted, "how God puts them there! First He makes them up above and then He drops them down. That was a new one." Then, lifting his head to the stars, he cried: "Oh, God, do it again, but slowly, so that I, Adam, may see."

But nothing happened, and the doolie-bearers lit the noisome, dripping rag-torches, and Adam's eyes shone big in the dancing light, and we smelt the dry dust of the plains that we were leaving after eleven months' hard work.

At stated times the men ceased their drowsy, grunting tune, and sat down for a smoke. Between the guttering of their water-pipes we could hear the cries of the beasts of the night, and the wind stirring in the folds of the mountain ahead. At the changing-station the voice of Adam, the First of Men, would be lifted to rouse the sleepers in the huts till the fresh relay of bearers shambled from their cots and the relief pony with them.

Then we would re-form and go on, and by the time the moon rose Adam was asleep, and there was no sound in the night except the grunting of the men, the husky murmur of some river a thousand feet down in the valley, and the squeaking of Strickland's saddle. So we went up from date-palm to deodar, till the dawn wind came round a corner all fresh from the snows, and we snuffed it.   I heard Strickland say, " Wife, my overcoat, please," and Adam, fretfully, " Where is Dalhousie and the cow's child?"   Then I slept till Strickland turned me out of the warm doolie at seven o'clock, and I stepped into all the splendour of a cool Hill day, the Plains sweltering twenty miles back and four thousand feet below.   Adam waked too, and needs must ride in front of me to ask a million questions, and shout at the monkeys and clap his hands when the painted pheasants bolted across our road, and hail every woodcutter and drover and pilgrim within sight, till we halted for breakfast at a rest house.   After that, being a child, he went out to play with a train of bullock-drivers halted by the roadside, and we had to chase him out of a native liquor shop, where he was bargaining with a native seven-year-old for a parrot in a bamboo cage.

Said he, wriggling on my pommel as we went on again, " There were four men *behosh* [insensible] at the back of that house.   Wherefore do men grow *behosh* from drinking?"

" It is the nature of the waters," I said, and, calling back, " Strick, what's that grog-shop doing so close to the road?   It's a temptation to any one's servants."

" Dunno," said a sleepy voice in the doolie. " This is Kennedy's District.   'Twasn't here in *my* time."

" Truly the waters smell bad," Adam went on.
" I smelt them, but I did not get the parrot even
for six annas.   The woman of the house gave me
a love gift that I found playing near the verandah."

" And what was the gift, Father Adam?"

" A nose-ring for my ayah.   Ohe!   Ohe!
Look at that camel with the muzzle on his nose!"

A string of loaded camels came cruising round
the corner as a fleet rounds a cape.

" Ho, Malik!   Why does not a camel salaam
like an elephant?   His neck is long enough,"
Adam cried.

" The Angel Jibrail made him a fool at the
beginning," said the driver, as he swayed on the
top of the leading beast, and laughter ran all along
the line of red-bearded men.

" That is true," said Adam solemnly, and they
laughed again.

At last, in the late afternoon, we came to
Dalhousie, the loveliest of the hill-stations, and
separated, Adam hardly able to be restrained from
setting out at once to find Victor and the " cow's
child."   I found them both, something to my
trouble, next morning.   The two young sinners
had a calf on a tight rope just at a sharp turn in the
Mall, and were pretending that he was a raja's
elephant who had gone mad; and they shouted
with delight.   Then we began to talk, and Adam,
by way of crushing Victor's repeated reminders to

me that he and not " that other " was the owner
of the calf, said, " It is true I have no cow's child;
but a great *dacoity* [robbery] has been done on my
father."

" We came up together yesterday.   There
could have been nothing," I said.

" It was my mother's horse.   She has been
dacoited with beating and blows, and now is *so*
thin."   He held his hands an inch apart.   " My
father is at the telegraph-house sending telegrams.
Imam Din will cut off *all* their heads.   I desire
your saddle-cloth for a howdah for my elephant.
Give it me!"

This was exciting, but not lucid.   I went to
the telegraph office and found Strickland in a
black temper among many telegraph forms.   A
dishevelled, one-eyed groom stood in a corner
whimpering at intervals.   He was a man whom
Adam invariably addressed as " *Be-shakl, be-ukl,
be-ank* " [ugly, stupid, eyeless].   It seemed that
Strickland had sent his wife's horse up to Dalhousie
by road, a fortnight's march, in the groom's charge.
This is the custom in Upper India.   Among the
foot-hills, near Dhunnera or Dhar, horse and man
had been violently set upon in the night by four men,
who had beaten the groom (his leg was bandaged
from knee to ankle in proof), had incidentally
beaten the horse, and had robbed the groom of the
bucket and blanket, and all his money—eleven

rupees, nine annas.   Last, they had left him for dead by the wayside, where some woodcutters had found and nursed him.   Then the one-eyed man howled with anguish, thinking over his bruises. " They asked me if I was Strickland Sahib's servant, and I, thinking the Protection of the Name would be sufficient, spoke the truth.   Then they beat me grievously."

" H'm!" said Strickland.   " I thought they wouldn't dacoit as a business on the Dalhousie road.   This is meant for me personally—sheer *badmashi* [impudence].   All right."

In justice to a very hard-working class it must be said that the thieves of Upper India have the keenest sense of humour.   The last compliment that they can pay a Police officer is to rob him, and if, as once they did, they can loot a Deputy Inspector-General of Police, on the eve of his retirement, of everything except the clothes on his back, their joy is complete.   They cause letters of derision and telegrams of condolence to be sent to the victim; for of all men thieves are most compelled to keep abreast of progress.

Strickland was a man of few words where his business was concerned.   I had never seen a Police officer robbed before, and I expected some excitement, but Strickland held his tongue.   He took the groom's deposition, and then retired into himself for a time.   Then he sent Kennedy, of the

Pathankot District, an official letter and an un-official note. Kennedy's reply was purely un-official, and it ran thus: " This seems a compli-ment solely intended for you.   My wonder is you didn't get it before.   The men are probably back in your district by now.   My Dhunnera and foot-hill people are highly respectable cultivators, and, seeing my Assistant is an unlicked pup, and I can't trust my Inspector out of my sight, I'm not going to turn their harvest upside down with Police investigations.   I'm run off my feet with vaccination Police work.   You'd better look at home.   The Shubkudder Gang were through here a fortnight back.   They laid up at the Amritsar Serai, and then worked down.   No cases against them in my charge; but, remember, you imprisoned their head-man for receiving stolen goods in Prub Dyal's burglary.   They owe you one."

" Exactly what I thought," said Strickland. " I had a notion it *was* the Shubkudder Gang from the first.   We must make it pleasant for them at Peshawur, and in my District, too.   They're just the kind that would lie up under Imam Din's shadow."

From this point onward the wires began to be worked heavily.   Strickland had a very fair knowledge of the Shubkudder Gang, gathered at first hand.

R

They were the same syndicate that had once stolen a Deputy Commissioner's cow, put horse-shoes on her, and taken her forty miles into the jungle before they lost interest in the joke. They added insult to insult by writing that the Deputy Commissioner's cows and horses were so much alike that it took them two days to find out the difference and they would not lift the like of such cattle any more.

The District Superintendent at Peshawur replied to Strickland that he was expecting the Gang, and Strickland's Assistant, in his own district, being young and full of zeal, sent up the most amazing clues.

" Now that's just what I want that young fool not to do," said Strickland. " He's an English boy, born and bred, and his father before him. He has about as much tact as a bull, and he won't work quietly under my Inspector. I wish the Government would keep our service for country-born men. Those first five or six years in India give a man a pull that lasts him all his life. Adam, if only you were old enough to be my Assistant!" He looked down at the little fellow in the verandah. Adam was deeply interested in the dacoity, and, unlike a child, did not lose interest after the first week. On the contrary, he would ask his father every evening what had been done, and Strickland had drawn him a map on the white wall of the verandah, showing the different towns in which Policemen were on the look-out for thieves. They were Amritsar, Jullunder, Phillour, Gurgaon, Rawal Pindi, Peshawur and Multan. Adam looked up at it as he answered—

" There has been great *dikh* [trouble] in this case?"

" Very great trouble. I wish that thou wert a young man and my Assistant to help me."

" Dost thou need help, my father?" Adam asked curiously, with his head on one side.

" Very much."

" Leave it all alone. It is bad. Let loose everything."

" That must not be. Those beginning a business continue to the end."

" Thou wilt continue to the end? Dost thou not *know* who did the dacoity?"

Strickland shook his head. Adam turned to me with the same question, and I answered it in the same way.

" What foolish people!" he said, and turned his back on us.

He showed plainly in all our dealings afterwards how we had fallen in his opinion. Strickland told me that he would sit at the door of his father's workroom and stare at him for half an hour at a time as he went through his papers. Strickland seemed to work harder

over the case than if he had been in office in
the Plains.

"And sometimes I look up and I fancy the
little chap's laughing at me. It's an awful thing
to have a son. You see, he's your own and *his*
own, and between the two you don't quite know
how to handle him," said Strickland. "I wonder
what in the world he thinks about."

I asked Adam this later on, quietly. He put
his head on one side for a moment and replied:
"In these days I think about great things. I do
not play with Victor and the cow's child any more.
Victor is only a baba."

At the end of the third week of Strickland's
leave, the result of Strickland's labours—labours
that had made Mrs. Strickland more indignant
against the dacoits than any one else—came to
hand. The Police at Peshawur reported that
half of the Shubkudder Gang were held at Peshawur to account for the possession of some blankets
and a horse-bucket. Strickland's assistant had
also four men under suspicion in his charge; and
Imam Din must have stirred up Strickland's
Inspector to investigations on his own account,
for a string of incoherent telegrams came in from
the Club Secretary in which he entreated, exhorted,
and commanded Strickland to take his "mangy
Policemen" off the Club premises. "Your
men, in servants' quarters here, examining cook.

Billiard - marker indignant.   Steward threatens resignation.   Members furious.   Grooms stopped on roads.   Shut up, or my resignation goes to Committee."

" Now I shouldn't in the least wonder," said Strickland thoughtfully to his wife, " if the Club was not just *the* place where the men would lie up.   Billy Watson isn't at all pleased, though.   I think I shall have to cut my leave by a week and go down to take charge.   If there's anything to be told, the men will tell me."

Mrs. Strickland's eyes filled with tears.   " I shall try to steal ten days if I can in the autumn," he said soothingly, " but I must go now.   It will never do for the gang to think that they can burgle *my* belongings."

That was in the forenoon, and Strickland asked me to lunch to leave me some instructions about his big dog, with authority to rebuke those who did not attend to her.   *Tietjens* was growing too old and too fat to live in the plains in the summer. When I came, Adam had climbed into his high chair at table, and Mrs. Strickland seemed ready to weep at any moment over the general misery of things.

" I go down to the Plains to-morrow, my son," said Strickland.

" Wherefore?" said Adam, reaching out for a ripe mango and burying his head in it.

" Imam Din has caught the men who did the dacoity, and there are also others at Peshawur under suspicion.   I must go to see."

" *Bus!* [enough]," said Adam, between sucks at his mango, as Mrs. Strickland tucked the napkin round his neck.   " Imam Din speaks lies. Do not go."

" It is necessary.   There has been great *dikh-dari* [trouble-giving]."

Adam came out of the fruit for a minute and laughed.   Then, returning, he spoke between slow and deliberate mouthfuls.

" The dacoits live in Beshakl's head.   They will never be caught.   All people know that. The cook knows, and the scullion, and Rahim Baksh here."

" Nay," said the butler behind his chair hastily. " What should *I* know?   Nothing at all does the Servant of the Presence know."

" *Accha* [good]," said Adam, and sucked on. " Only it *is* known."

" Speak, then, son," said Strickland to him. " What dost thou know?   Remember my groom was beaten insensible."

" That was in the bad-water shop where I played when we came up here.   The boy who would not sell me the parrot for six annas told me that a one-eyed man had come there and drunk the bad waters and gone mad.   He broke bedsteads.

They hit him with a bamboo till he was senseless,
and fearing he was dead, they nursed him on milk
—like a little baba. When I was playing first with
the cow's child, I asked Beshakl if he were that
man, and he said no. But *I* knew, because many
woodcutters in Dalhousie asked him whether his
head were whole now."

"But why," I interrupted, "did Beshakl tell
lies?"

"Oh! He is a low-caste man, and desired to
get consideration. Now he is a witness in a great
law-case, and men will go to the jail on his account.
It was to give trouble and obtain notice that he
did it."

"Was it all lies?" said Strickland.

"Ask him," said Adam, through the mango-
pulp.

Strickland passed through the door. There
was a howl of despair in the servants' quarters
up the hill, and he returned with the one-eyed
groom.

"Now," said Strickland, "it is known. De-
clare!"

"Beshakl," said Adam, while the man gasped.
"Imam Din has caught four men, and there are
some more at Peshawur. *Bus! Bus! Bus!*
[Enough.]"

"Thou didst get drunk by the wayside, and
didst make a false case to cover it. Speak!"

Like a good many other men, Strickland, in possession of a few facts, was irresistible. The groom groaned.

" I—I did not get drunk till—till—Protector of the Poor, the mare rolled."

" *All* horses roll at Dhunnera. The road is too narrow before that, and they smell where the other horses have rolled. This the bullock-drivers told me when we came up here," said Adam.

" She rolled. So her saddle was cut and the curb-chain lost."

" See!" said Adam, tugging a curb-chain from his pocket. " That woman in the shop gave it to me for a love-gift. Beshakl said it was not his when I showed it. But *I* knew."

" Then they at the grog-shop, knowing that I was the Servant of the Presence, said that unless I drank and spent money they would tell."

" A lie! A lie!" said Strickland. " Son of an owl, speak the truth now at least."

" Then I was afraid because I had lost the curb-chain, so I cut the saddle across and about."

" She did *not* roll, then?" said Strickland, bewildered and angry.

" It was only the curb-chain that was lost. Then I cut the saddle and went to drink in the shop. I drank and there was a fray. The rest I have forgotten till I recovered."

" And the mare the while? What of the mare?"

The man looked at Strickland and collapsed.

" She bore faggots for a week," he said.

" Oh, poor *Diamond*!" said Mrs. Strickland.

" And Beshakl was paid four annas for her hire three days ago by the woodcutter's brother, who is the left-hand man of our rickshaw-men here," said Adam, in a loud and joyful voice. " We *all* knew. We all knew. I and the servants."

Strickland was silent. His wife stared help-lessly at the child; the soul out of Nowhere that went its own way alone.

" Did no man help thee with the lies?" I asked of the groom.

" None. Protector of the Poor—not one."

" They grew, then?"

" As a tale grows in telling. Alas! I am a very bad man!" and he blinked his one eye dolefully.

" Now four men are held at my Police station on thy account, and God knows how many more at Peshawur, besides the questions at Multan, and my honour is lost, and my mare has been pack-pony to a woodcutter. Son of Devils, what canst thou do to make amends?"

There was just a little break in Strickland's voice, and the man caught it. Bending low, he answered, in the abject fawning whine that confounds right and wrong more surely than most modern creeds, " Protector of the Poor, is the Police service shut to—an honest man?"

" Out!" cried Strickland, and swiftly as the groom departed he must have heard our shouts of laughter behind him.

" If you dismiss that man, Strick, I shall engage him. He's a genius," said I. " It will take you months to put this mess right, and Billy Watson won't give you a minute's peace."

" You aren't going to tell him?" said Strickland appealingly.

" I couldn't keep this to myself if you were my own brother. Four men arrested with you—four or forty at Peshawur—and what was that you said about Multan?"

" Oh, nothing. Only some camel-men there have been———"

" And a tribe of camel-men at Multan! All on account of a lost curb-chain. Oh, my Aunt!"

" And whose memsahib [lady] was thy aunt?" said Adam, with the mango-stone in his fist. We began to laugh again.

" But here," said Strickland, pulling his face together, " is a very bad child who has caused his father to lose his honour before all the Policemen of the Punjab."

" Oh, *they* know," said Adam. " It was only

for the sake of show that they caught people. Assuredly they all knew it was *benowti* [make-up]."

" And since when hast thou known?" said the first policeman in India to his son.

" Four days after we came here, after the wood-cutter had asked Beshakl after the health of his head.   Beshakl all but slew one of them at the bad-water place."

" If thou hadst spoken then, time and money and trouble to me and to others had all been spared.   Baba, thou hast done a wrong greater than thy knowledge, and thou hast put me to shame, and set me out upon false words, and broken my honour.   Thou hast done *very* wrong. But perhaps thou didst not think?"

" Nay, but I *did* think.   My father, *my* honour was lost when that beating of me happened in Juma's presence.   Now it is made whole again."

And with the most enchanting smile in the world Adam climbed up on to his father's lap.

AN ENGLISH SCHOOL

AN ENGLISH SCHOOL

OF all things in the world there is nothing, always excepting a good mother, so worthy of honour as a good school. Our School was created for the sons of officers in the Army and Navy, and filled with boys who meant to follow their father's calling.

It stood within two miles of Amyas Leigh's house at Northam, overlooking the Burroughs and the Pebble-ridge, and the mouth of the Torridge whence the *Rose* sailed in search of Don Guzmán. From the front dormitory windows, across the long rollers of the Atlantic, you could see Lundy Island and the Shutter Rock, where the *Santa Catherina* galleon cheated Amyas out of his vengeance by going ashore. If you have ever read Kingsley's *Westward Ho!* you will remember how all these things happened.

Inland lay the rich Devonshire lanes and the fat orchards, and to the west the gorse and the turf ran along the tops of the cliffs in combe after combe till you come to Clovelly and the Hobby and Gallantry Bower, and the homes of the

Devonshire people that were old when the Armada was new.

The Burroughs, lying between the school and the sea, was a waste of bent rush and grass running out into hundreds of acres of fascinating sand-hills called the Bunkers, where a few old people played golf. In the early days of the School there was a small Club-house for golfers close to the Pebble-ridge, but, one wild winter night, the sea got up and drove the Pebble-ridge clean through the Club basement, and the walls fell out, and we rejoiced, for even then golfers wore red coats and did not like us to use the links. We played as a matter of course and thought nothing of it.

Now there is a new Club-house, and cars take the old, red, excited men to and from their game and all the great bunkers are known and written about; but we were there first, long before golf became a fashion or a disease, and we turned out one of the earliest champion amateur golfers of all England.

It was a good place for a school, and that School considered itself the finest in the world, excepting perhaps Haileybury, because it was modelled on Haileybury lines and our caps were Haileybury colours; and there was a legend that, in the old days when the School was new, half the boys had been Haileyburians.

Our Head-master had been Head of the
Modern Side at Haileybury, and, talking it over
with boys from other public schools afterwards, I
think that one secret of his great hold over us was
that he was not a clergyman, as so many head-
masters are.   As soon as a boy begins to think in
the misty way that boys do, he is suspicious of a
man who punishes him one day and preaches at
him the next.   But the Head was different, and
in our different ways we loved him.

Through all of five years I never saw him lose
his temper, nor among two hundred boys did any
one at any time say or hint that he had his
favourites.   If you went to him with any trouble
you were heard out to the end, and answered
without being talked at or about or around, but
always *to*.   So we trusted him absolutely, and
when it came to the choice of the various ways of
entering the Army, what he said was so.

He knew boys naturally better than their
fathers knew them, and considerably better than
they knew themselves.   When the time came to
read for the Final Army Examinations, he knew
the temper and powers of each boy, the amount of
training each would stand and the stimulus or
restraint that each needed, and handled them
accordingly till they had come through the big
race that led into the English Army.   Looking
back on it all, one can see the perfect judgment,

s

knowledge of boys, patience, and above all, power, that the Head must have had.

Some of the masters, particularly on the classical side, vowed that Army examinations were making education no more than mark-hunting; but there are a great many kinds of education, and I think the Head knew it, for he taught us hosts of things that we never found out we knew till afterwards. And surely it must be better to turn out men who do real work than men who write about what they think about what other people have done or ought to do.

A scholar may, as the Latin masters said, get more pleasure out of his life than an Army officer, but only little children believe that a man's life is given him to decorate with pretty little things, as though it were a girl's room or a picture-screen. Besides, scholars are apt, all their lives, to judge from one point of view only, and by the time that an Army officer has knocked about the world for a few years he comes to look at men and things " by and large," as the sailors say. No books in the world will teach that knack.

So we trusted the Head at school, and afterwards trusted him more.

There was a boy in the Canadian Mounted Police, I think, who stumbled into a fortune—he was the only one of us who ever did—and as he had never drawn more than seven shillings a day, he very properly wrote to the Head from out of his North-Western wilds and explained his situation, proposing that the Head should take charge of and look after all his wealth till he could attend to it; and was a little impatient when the Head pointed out that executors and trustees and that sort of bird wouldn't hand over cash in that casual way. The Head was worth trusting—he saved a boy's life from diphtheria once at much greater risk than being shot at, and nobody knew anything about it till years afterwards.

But I come back to the School that he made and put his mark upon. The boys said that those with whom Cheltenham could do nothing, whom Sherbourne found too tough, and whom even Marlborough had politely asked to leave, had been sent to the School at the beginning of things and turned into men. They were, perhaps, a shade rough sometimes. One very curious detail, which I have never seen or heard of in any school before or since, was that the Army Class, which meant the Prefects, and was generally made up of boys from seventeen and a half to nineteen or thereabouts, was allowed to smoke pipes (cigarettes were then reckoned the direct invention of the Evil One) in the country outside the College. One result of this was that, though these great men talked a good deal about the grain of their pipes, the beauty of their pouches, and the flavour

of their tobacco, they did not smoke to any
ferocious extent. The other, which concerned
me more directly, was that it went much harder
with a junior whom they caught smoking than if
he had been caught by a master, because the
action was flagrant invasion of their privilege, and,
therefore, rank insolence—to be punished as such.
Years later, the Head admitted that he thought
something of this kind would happen when he
gave the permission. If any Head-master is
anxious to put down smoking nowadays, he might
do worse than give this scheme a trial.

The School motto was, " Fear God, Honour
the King "; and so the men she made went out
to Boerland and Zululand and India and Burma
and Cyprus and Hongkong, and lived or died as
gentlemen and officers.

Even the most notorious bully, for whom an
awful ending was prophesied, went to Canada and
was mixed up in Riel's rebellion, and came out of
it with a fascinating reputation of having led a
forlorn hope and behaved like a hero.

All these matters were noted by the older boys,
and when their fathers, the grey-whiskered
colonels and generals, came down to see them, or
the directors, who were K.C.B.'s and had been
officers in their time, made a tour of inspection, it
was reported that the School tone was " healthy."

Sometimes an old boy who had blossomed into

a Subaltern of the Queen would come down for a
last few words with the Head-master, before sailing
with the regiment for foreign parts; and the
lower-school boys were distracted with envy, and
the prefects of the Sixth Form pretended not to
be proud when he walked with one of their
number and talked about " my men, you know,"
till life became unendurable.

There was an unwritten law by which an old
boy, when he came back to pay his respects to
the School, was entitled to a night in his old
dormitory.   The boys expected it and sat up half
the night listening to the tales of a subaltern that
the boy brought with him—stories about riots in
Ireland and camps at Aldershot, and all his first
steps in the wonderful world.

Sometimes news came in that a boy had died
with his men fighting, and the school said,
" Killed in action, of course," as though that were
an honour reserved for it alone, and wondered
when its own chance would come.

It was a curiously quiet School in many ways.
When a boy was fourteen or fifteen he was generally taken in hand for the Army Preliminary
Examination, and when that was past he was put
down to " grind " for the entrance into Sandhurst
or Woolwich; for it was our pride that we passed
direct from the School to the Army, without
troubling the " crammers."   We spoke of " the

Shop," which means Woolwich, as though we owned it. Sandhurst was our private reserve; and the old boys came back from foreign parts and told us that India was only Westward Ho! spread thin.

On account of this incessant getting ready for examinations there was hardly time for us (but we made it) to gather the beautiful Devonshire apples, or to ferret rabbits in the sand-hills by the golf-links, and saloon-pistols were forbidden because boys got to duelling-parties with dust-shot, and were careless about guarding their eyes.

Nor were we encouraged to lower each other over the cliffs with a box-rope and take the young hawks and jackdaws from their nests above the sea. Once a rope broke, or else the boys above grew tired of holding it, and a boy dropped thirty feet on to the boulders below. But as he fell on his head nothing happened, except punishment at the other end for all concerned.

In summer there was almost unlimited bathing from the Pebble-ridge, a whale-backed bank four miles long of rounded grey boulders, where you were taught to ride on the rollers as they came in, to avoid the under-tow, and to watch your time for getting back to the beach.

There was a big sea bath, too, in which all boys had to qualify for open bathing by swimming a quarter of a mile, at least; and it was a

matter of honour among the school-houses not to
let the summer end with a single boy who could
not " do his quarter," at any rate.

Boating was impossible off that coast, but
sometimes a fishing-boat would be wrecked on
Braunton Bar, and we could see the lifeboat and
the rocket at work; and once just after chapel
there was a cry that the herring were in. The
School ran down to the beach in their Sunday
clothes and fished them out with umbrellas.
They were cooked by hand afterwards in all the
studies and form-rooms till you could have smelt
us at Exeter.

But the game of the School, setting aside golf,
which every one could play if he had patience,
was foot-ball. Both cricket and foot-ball were
compulsory. That is to say, unless a boy could
show a doctor's certificate that he was physically
unfit to stand up to the wicket or go into the
scrimmage, he had to play a certain number of
afternoons at the game of the season. If he had
engagements elsewhere—we called it " shirking "
—he was reasonably sure of three cuts with a
ground-ash, from the Captain of the Games, delivered cold in the evening. A good player, of
course, could get leave off on any fair excuse, but
it was a beautiful rule for fat boys and loafers.
The only unfairness was that a Master could load
you with an imposition to be shown up at a certain

hour, which, of course, prevented you from playing and so secured you a licking in addition to
the imposition.   But the Head always told us
that there was not much justice in the world, and
that we had better accustom ourselves to the lack
of it early.

Curiously enough, the one thing that the
School did not understand was an attempt to drill
it in companies with rifles, by way of making a
volunteer cadet corps.   We took our lickings for
not attending *that* cheerfully, because we considered it " playing at soldiers," and boys reading
for the Army are apt to be very particular on these
points.

We were weak at cricket, but our foot-ball
team (Rugby Union) at its best devastated the
country from Blundell's—we always respected
Blundell's because " Great John Ridd " had been
educated there—to Exeter, whose team were
grown men.   Yet we, who had been taught to
play together, once drove them back over the
November mud, back to their own goal-posts, till
the ball was hacked through and touched down,
and you could hear the long-drawn yell of " Schoo-
ool!   Schoo-ool!" as far as Appledore.

When the enemy would not come to us our
team went to the enemy, and if victorious, would
return late at night in a three-horse brake,
chanting:

It's a way we have in the Army,
It's a way we have in the Navy,
It's a way we have in the Public Schools,
Which nobody can deny!

Then the boys would flock to the dormitory windows, and wave towels and join in the " Hip-hip-hip-hurrah!" of the chorus, and the winning team would swagger through the dormitories and show the beautiful blue marks on their shins, and the little boys would be allowed to get the sponges and hot water.

Very few things that the world can offer make up for having missed a place in the First Fifteen, with its black jersey and white—snow-white—knickerbockers, and the velvet skull-cap with the gold tassel—the cap that you leave out in the rain and accidentally step upon to make it look as old as if you had been in the First Fifteen for years.

The other outward sign of the First Fifteen that the happy boy generally wore through a hard season was the " jersey-mark "—a raw, red scrape on ear and jawbone where the skin had been fretted by the rough jerseys in either side in the steady drive of many scrimmages. We were trained to put our heads down, pack in the shape of a wedge and shove, and it was in that shape that the First Fifteen stood up to a team of trained men for two and twenty counted minutes. We got the ball through in the end.

At the close of the winter term, when there were no more foot-ball teams to squander and the Christmas holidays were coming, the School set itself to the regular yearly theatricals—a farce and a three-act play all complete. Sometimes it was *The Rivals*, or sometimes an attempt at a Shakespearean play; but the farces were the most popular.

All ended with the School-Saga, the "*Vive la Compagnie!*" in which the Senior boy of the School chanted the story of the School for the past twelve months. It was very long and very difficult to make up, though all the poets of all the forms had been at work on it for weeks; and the School gave the chorus at the top of its voice.

On the last Sunday of the term the last hymn in chapel was "Onward, Christian Soldiers." We did not know what it meant then, and we did not care, but we stood up and sang it till the music was swamped in the rush. The big verse, like the " tug-of-war " verse in Mrs. Ewing's *Story of a Short Life*, was:

> We are not divided,
>   All one body we,
>   One in faith and doctrine,
>   One in charity.

Then the organ would give a hurricane of joyful roars, and try to get us in hand before the refrain. Later on, meeting our men all the world over, the meaning of that hymn became much too plain.

Except for this outbreak we were not very pious. There was a boy who had to tell stories night after night in the Dormitory, and when his stock ran out he fell back on a book called *Eric, or Little by Little,* as comic literature, and read it till the gas was turned off. The boys laughed abominably, and there was some attempt to give selections from it at the meeting of the Reading Society. That was quashed by authority because it was against discipline.

There were no public-houses near us except tap-rooms that sold cider; and raw Devonshire cider can only be drunk after a long and very hot paper-chase. We hardly ever saw, and certainly never spoke to, anything in the nature of a woman from one year's end to the other; for our masters were all unmarried. Later on, a little colony of mothers came down to live near the School, but their sons were day-boys who couldn't do this and mustn't do that, and there was a great deal too much dressing up on week-days and going out to tea, and things of that kind, which, whatever people say nowadays, are not helpful for boys at work.

Our masters, luckily, were never gushing. They did not call us Dickie or Johnnie or Tommy, but Smith or Thompson; and when we were undoubtedly bad we were actually and painfully beaten with an indubitable cane on a veritable back till we wept unfeigned tears. Nobody seemed to think that it brutalized our finer feelings, but everybody was relieved when the trouble was over.

Canes, especially when they are brought down with a drawing stroke, sting like hornets; but they are a sound cure for certain offences; and a cut or two, given with no malice, but as a reminder, can correct and keep corrected a false quantity or a wandering mind, more completely than any amount of explanation.

There was one boy, however, to whom every Latin quantity was an arbitrary mystery, and he wound up his crimes by suggesting that he could do better if Latin verse rhymed as decent verse should. He was given an afternoon's reflection to purge himself of his contempt; and feeling certain that he was in for something rather warm, he turned " *Donec gratus eram* " into pure Devonshire dialect, rhymed, and showed it up as his contribution to the study of Horace.

He was let off, and his master gave him the run of a big library, where he found as much verse and prose as he wanted; but that ruined his Latin verses and made him write verses of his own. There he found all the English poets from Chaucer to Matthew Arnold, and a book called *Imaginary Conversations* which he did not understand, but it seemed to be a good thing to imitate. So he imitated and was handed up to the Head, who said that he had better learn Russian under his own eye, so that if ever he were sent to Siberia for lampooning the authorities he might be able to ask for things.

That meant the run of another library—English Dramatists this time; hundreds of old plays; as well as thick brown books of voyages told in language like the ringing of bells. And the Head would sometimes tell him about the manners and customs of the Russians, and sometimes about his own early days at college, when several people who afterwards became great, were all young, and the Head was young with them, and they wrote wonderful things in college magazines.

It was beautiful and cheap—dirt cheap, at the price of a permanent load of impositions, for neglecting mathematics and algebra.

The School started a Natural History Society, which took the birds and plants of North Devon under its charge, reporting first flowerings and first arrivals and new discoveries to learned societies in London, and naturally attracting to itself every boy in the School who had the poaching instinct.

Some of us made membership an excuse for stealing apples and pheasant eggs and geese from farmers' orchards and gentlemen's estates, and we were turned out with disgrace. So we spoke scornfully of the Society ever afterwards. None the less, some of us had our first introduction to gun-powder in the shape of a charge of salt which stings like bees, fired at our legs by angry game-keepers.

The institution that caused some more excite-ment was the School paper. Three of the boys, who had moved up the School side by side for four years and were allies in all things, started the notion as soon as they came to the dignity of a study of their own with a door that would lock. The other two told the third boy what to write, and held the staircase against invaders.

It was a real printed paper of eight pages, and at first the printer was more thoroughly ignorant of type-setting, and the Editor was more com-pletely ignorant of proof-reading, than any printer and any Editor that ever was. It was printed off by a gas engine; and even the engine despised its work, for one day it fell through the floor of the shop, and crashed—still working furiously—into the cellar.

The paper came out at odd times and seasons, but every time it came out there was sure to be trouble, because the Editor was learning for the first time how sweet and good and profitable it is—and how nice it looks on the page—to make fun of people in actual print.

For instance, there was friction among the study-fags once, and the Editor wrote a descriptive account of the Lower School,—the classes whence the fags were drawn,—their manners and customs, their ways of cooking half-plucked sparrows and imperfectly cleaned blackbirds at the gas-jets on a rusty nib, and their fights over sloe-jam made in a gallipot. It was an absolutely truthful article, but the Lower School knew nothing about truth, and would not even consider it as literature.

It is less safe to write a study of an entire class than to discuss individuals one by one; but apart from the fact that boys throw books and inkpots with a straighter eye, there is very little difference between the behaviour of grown-up people and that of children.

In those days the Editor had not learned this; so when the study below the Editorial study threw coal at the Editorial legs and kicked in the panels of the door, because of personal paragraphs in the last number, the Editorial Staff—and there never was so loyal and hard-fighting a staff— fried fat bacon till there was half an inch of grease in the pan, and let the greasy chunks down at the end of a string to bob against and defile the lower study windows.

When that lower study—and there never was a public so low and unsympathetic as that lower study—looked out to see what was frosting their window-panes, the Editorial Staff emptied the hot fat on their heads, and it stayed in their hair for days and days, wearing shiny to the very last.

The boy who suggested this sort of warfare was then reading a sort of magazine, called *Fors Clavigera*, which he did not in the least understand,—it was not exactly a boy's paper,—and when the lower study had scraped some of the fat off their heads and were thundering with knobby pokers on the door-lock, this boy began to chant pieces of the *Fors* as a war-song, and to show that his mind was free from low distractions. He was an extraordinary person, and the only boy in the School who had a genuine contempt for his masters. There was no affectation in his quiet insolence. He honestly *did* despise them; and threats that made us all wince only caused him to put his head a little on one side and watch the master as a sort of natural curiosity.

The worst of this was that his allies had to take their share of his punishments, for they lived as communists and socialists hope to live one day, when everybody is good. They were bad, as bad as they dared to be, but their possessions were in common, absolutely. And when " the Study " was out of funds they took the most respectable clothes in possession of the Syndicate, and leaving the owner one Sunday and one weekday suit, sold the rest in Bideford town. Later, when there was another crisis, it was *not* the respectable one's watch that was taken by force for the good of the Study and pawned, and never redeemed.

Later still, money came into the Syndicate honestly, for a London paper that did not know with whom it was dealing, published and paid a whole guinea for some verses that one of the boys had written and sent up under a *nom de plume*, and the Study caroused on chocolate and condensed milk and pilchards and Devonshire cream, and voted poetry a much sounder business than it looks.

So things went on very happily till the three were seriously warned that they must work in earnest, and stop giving amateur performances of *Aladdin* and writing librettos of comic operas which never came off, and worrying their house-masters into grey hairs.

Then they all grew very good, and one of them got into the Army; and another—the Irish one—became an engineer, and the third one found himself on a daily paper half a world away from the Pebble Ridge and the sea-beach. The three swore eternal friendship before they parted, and from time to time they met boys of their year in India, and magnified the honour of the old School.

T

The boys are scattered all over the world, one to each degree of land east and west, as their fathers were before them, doing much the same kind of work; and it is curious to notice how little the character of the man differs from that of the boy of sixteen or seventeen.

The general and commander-in-chief of the Study, he who suggested selling the clothes, never lost his head even when he and his friends were hemmed round by the enemy—the Drill Sergeant—far out of bounds and learning to smoke under a hedge. He was sick and dizzy, but he rose to the occasion, took command of his forces, and by strategic manœuvres along dry ditches and crawlings through tall grass, out-flanked the enemy and got into safe ground without losing one man of the three.

A little later, when he was a subaltern in India, he was bitten by a mad dog, went to France to be treated by Pasteur, and came out again in the heat of the hot weather to find himself almost alone in charge of six hundred soldiers, and his Drill Sergeant dead and his office clerk run away, leaving the Regimental books in the most ghastly confusion. Then we happened to meet; and as he was telling his story there was just the same happy look on his face as when he steered us down the lanes with the certainty of a superior thrashing if we were caught.

And there were others who went abroad with their men, and when they got into tight places behaved very much as they had behaved at football.

The boy who used to take flying jumps on to the ball and roll over and over with it, because he was big and fat and could not run, took a flying jump on to a Burmese dacoit whom he had surprised by night in a stockade; but he forgot that he was much heavier than he had been at School, and by the time he rolled off his victim the little dacoit was stone dead.

And there was a boy who was always being led astray by bad advice, and begging off punishment on that account. He got into some little scrape when he grew up, and we who knew him knew, before he was reprimanded by his commanding officer, exactly what his excuse would be. It came out almost word for word as he was used to whimper it at School. He was cured, though, by being sent off on a small expedition where he alone would be responsible for any advice that was going, as well as for fifty soldiers.

And the best boy of them all—who could have become anything—was wounded in the thigh as he was leading his men up the ramp of a fortress. All he said was, " Put me up against that tree and take my men on "; and when his men came back he was dead.

T 2

Ages and ages ago, when Queen Victoria was shot at by a man in the street, the School paper made some verses about it that ended like this:

> One school of many, made to make
>   Men who shall hold it dearest right
> To battle for their ruler's sake,
>   And stake their being in the fight,
>
> Sends greeting, humble and sincere,
>   Though verse be rude and poor and mean,
> To you, the greatest as most dear,
>   Victoria, by God's Grace, our Queen!
>
> Such greetings as should come from those
>   Whose fathers faced the Sepoy hordes,
> Or served you in the Russian snows
>   And dying, left their sons their swords.
>
> For we are bred to do your will
>   By land and sea, wherever flies
> The Flag to fight and follow still,
>   And work your empire's destinies.
>
> Once more we greet you, though unseen
>   Our greetings be, and coming slow.
> Trust us, if need arise, O Queen!
>   We shall not tarry with the blow.

And there are one or two places in the world that can bear witness how the School kept its word.

A COUNTING-OUT SONG

A COUNTING-OUT SONG

WHAT is the song the children sing
When doorway lilacs bloom in Spring,
And the Schools are loosed, and the games are
    played
That were deadly earnest when Earth was made?
Hear them chattering, shrill and hard,
After dinner-time, out in the yard,
As the sides are chosen and all submit
To the chance of the lot that shall make them
    " It."
  (Singing) " *Eenee, Meenee, Mainee, Mo!*
            Catch a nigger by the toe!
            If he hollers let him go
            Eenee, Meenee, Mainee, Mo!
            You—are—It!"

Eenee, Meenee, Mainee, and Mo
Were the First Big Four of the Long Ago,
When the Pole of the Earth sloped thirty degrees,
And Central Europe began to freeze,
And they needed Ambassadors staunch and stark
To steady the Tribes in the gathering dark:

But the frost was fierce and flesh was frail,
So they launched a Magic that could not fail.
  (Singing) " *Eenee, Meenee, Mainee, Mo!*
          Hear the wolves across the snow!
          Some one has to kill 'em—so
          Eenee, Meenee, Mainee, Mo
          Make—you—It!"

Slowly the Glacial Epoch passed,
Central Europe thawed out at last;
And, under the slush of the melting snows,
The first dim shapes of the Nations rose.
Rome, Britannia, Belgium, Gaul—
Flood and avalanche fathered them all;
And the First Big Four, as they watched the mess,
Pitied Man in his helplessness.
  (Singing) " *Eenee, Meenee, Mainee, Mo!*
          Trouble starts when Nations grow.
          Some one has to stop it—so
          Eenee, Meenee, Mainee, Mo
          Make—you—It!"

Thus it happened, but none can tell
What was the Power behind the spell—
Fear, or Duty, or Pride, or Faith—
That sent men shuddering out to death—
To cold and watching, and, worse than these,
Work, more work, when they looked for ease—

To the day's discomfort, the night's despair,
In the hope of a prize that they never would share.
  (Singing) " *Eenee, Meenee, Mainee, Mo!*
          Man is born to toil and woe.
          One will cure the other—so
          Eenee, Meenee, Mainee, Mo
          Make—you—It."

Once and again, as the Ice went North
The grass crept up to the Firth of Forth.
Once and again, as the Ice came South
The glaciers ground over Lossiemouth.
But, grass or glacier, cold or hot,
The men went out who would rather not,
And fought with the Tiger, the Pig and the Ape,
To hammer the world into decent shape.
  (Singing) " *Eenee, Meenee, Mainee, Mo!*
          What's the use of doing so?
          Ask the Gods, for we don't know;
          But Eenee, Meenee, Mainee, Mo
          Make—us—It!"

Nothing is left of that terrible rune
But a tag of gibberish tacked to a tune
That ends the waiting and settles the claims
Of children arguing over their games;
For never yet has a boy been found
To shirk his turn when the turn came round;

Or even a girl has been known to say
" If you laugh at me I shan't play."
For—   " *Eenee, Meenee, Mainee, Mo,*
            (Don't you let the grown-ups know!)
            You may hate it ever so,
            But if you're chose you're bound to go,
            When Eenee, Meenee, Mainee, Mo
            Make—you—It!"

THE END

Printed in Great Britain by R. & R. CLARK, LIMITED, *Edinburgh.*

THE WORKS OF RUDYARD KIPLING.

Uniform Edition. Extra Crown 8vo. Red Cloth, with Gilt Tops,
7s. 6d. net each.

Pocket Edition. Fcap. 8vo. Printed on Thin Paper, with Gilt Edges.
Scarlet Leather, 7s. 6d. net. Blue Cloth, 6s. net each.

PLAIN TALES FROM THE HILLS. One Hundred and Twenty-sixth
Thousand.
LIFE'S HANDICAP. Being Stories of Mine Own People.
One Hundredth Thousand.
MANY INVENTIONS. Ninety-fourth Thousand.
THE LIGHT THAT FAILED. One Hundred and Twenty-seventh Thousand.
WEE WILLIE WINKIE, and other Stories. Seventy-fourth Thousand.
SOLDIERS THREE, and other Stories. Eightieth Thousand.
"CAPTAINS COURAGEOUS." A Story of the Grand Banks.
Illustrated by I. W. TABER. Seventy-eighth Thousand.
THE JUNGLE BOOK. With Illustrations by J. L. KIPLING, W. H. DRAKE,
and P. FRENZENY. Two Hundred and Thirty-third Thousand.
THE DAY'S WORK. One Hundred and Thirty-fourth Thousand.
THE SECOND JUNGLE BOOK. With Illustrations by J. LOCKWOOD
KIPLING. One Hundred and Twenty-fifth Thousand.
STALKY & CO. One Hundred and Thirteenth Thousand.
FROM SEA TO SEA. Letters of Travel. In Two Vols. Forty-fifth
Thousand.
THE NAULAHKA. A Story of West and East. By RUDYARD
KIPLING and WOLCOTT BALESTIER. Forty-third Thousand.
KIM. With Illustrations by J. LOCKWOOD KIPLING. One Hundred and Seventy-
second Thousand.
JUST SO STORIES FOR LITTLE CHILDREN. With Illustrations
by the Author. One Hundred and Sixty-sixth Thousand.
TRAFFICS AND DISCOVERIES. Seventy-fourth Thousand.
PUCK OF POOK'S HILL. With Illustrations by H. R. MILLAR. Ninety-
ninth Thousand.
ACTIONS AND REACTIONS. Seventy-fourth Thousand.
REWARDS AND FAIRIES. With Illustrations by FRANK CRAIG.
Eighty-first Thousand.
SONGS FROM BOOKS. Fifty-sixth Thousand.
A DIVERSITY OF CREATURES. Sixty-fifth Thousand.
LETTERS OF TRAVEL (1892-1913). Twenty-seventh Thousand.

THE SERVICE KIPLING.

In 26 Vols. Blue Cloth. 16mo. 3s. net each.

PLAIN TALES FROM THE HILLS. 2 vols.
SOLDIERS THREE. 2 vols.
WEE WILLIE WINKIE. 2 vols.
FROM SEA TO SEA. 4 vols.
LIFE'S HANDICAP. 2 vols.
THE LIGHT THAT FAILED.
2 vols.

THE NAULAHKA. 2 vols.
MANY INVENTIONS. 2 vols.
THE DAY'S WORK. 2 vols.
KIM. 2 vols.
**TRAFFICS AND DISCOVER-
IES.** 2 vols.
ACTIONS AND REACTIONS.
2 vols.

MACMILLAN AND CO., LTD., LONDON.

THE WORKS OF RUDYARD KIPLING.

In Extra Gilt Cloth, Gilt Edges. 7s. 6d. *net each.*

CAPTAINS COURAGEOUS.

SOLDIER TALES. Fifteenth Thousand.

THE JUNGLE BOOK. | **SECOND JUNGLE BOOK.**

THE IRISH GUARDS IN THE GREAT WAR. Edited and compiled from their Diaries and Papers. With Maps and Plans. 2 vols. Medium 8vo. 40s. net.

A KIPLING ANTHOLOGY. **Prose.** Fcap. 8vo. Leather, 7s. 6d. net. Cloth, 6s. net.

LAND AND SEA TALES FOR SCOUTS AND GUIDES. Pott 4to. 4s. net.

THE JUNGLE BOOK. With Illustrations in Colour by MAURICE and EDWARD DETMOLD. 8vo. 10s. net.

LETTERS OF TRAVEL (1892-1913). *Edition de Luxe.* 8vo. 10s. 6d. net.

THE YEARS BETWEEN AND POEMS FROM HISTORY. *Edition de Luxe.* 8vo. 10s. 6d. net.

THE YEARS BETWEEN. THE MUSE AMONG THE MOTORS. *Bombay Edition.* 8vo. 21s. net.

A DIVERSITY OF CREATURES. *Bombay Edition.* Sup. royal 8vo. 21s. net. *Edition de Luxe.* 2 vols. 8vo. 10s. 6d. net each.

JUST SO STORIES FOR LITTLE CHILDREN. With Illustrations by the Author. Original Edition. 4to. 7s. 6d. net.

THE JUST SO SONG BOOK. Being the Songs from RUDYARD KIPLING'S *Just So Stories.* Set to Music by EDWARD GERMAN. Music Folio. Price 7s. 6d. net.

SEA WARFARE. Crown 8vo. 5s. net.

A FLEET IN BEING. Crown 8vo. Cloth, 1s. 6d. net. Paper, 1s. net.

INDEPENDENCE. Rectorial Address delivered at St. Andrews, October 10, 1923. Crown 8vo. 2s. net. Paper, 1s. net.

THE NEW ARMY IN TRAINING. 16mo. Paper. 6d. net.

FRANCE AT WAR. 16mo. Paper. 6d. net.

THE ARMY OF A DREAM. Crown 8vo. 6d. net.

DOCTORS. An Address. Crown 8vo. 1s. net.

IF ——. Pott 8vo. Paper, 1d. net. Also on Card, 3d. net.

THE CHILDREN'S SONG. Globe 8vo. Booklet. Paper, 1d. net. Leaflet, 2s. 6d. net per 100.

MACMILLAN AND CO., LTD., LONDON.

2